U.S. EDITION

PRIMARY MATHEMATICS 5A

TEXTBOOK

SingaporeMath.com Inc

Original edition published under the title Primary Mathematics Textbook 5A

Ministry of Education, Singapore
Published by Times Media Private Limited
This American Edition

Published by Marshall Cavendish Education
An imprint of Marshall Cavendish International (Singapore) Private Limited
Times Centre, 1 New Industrial Road, Singapore 536196
Customer Service Hotline: (65) 6411 0820
E-mail: fps@sg.marshallcavendish.com
Website: www.marshallcavendish.com/education/sg

Distributed by
SingaporeMath.com Inc
404 Beavercreek Road #225
Oregon City, OR 97045
U.S.A.
Website: http://www.singaporemath.com

First published 2003
Second impression 2003
Third impression 2005
Reprinted 2004
Fourth impression 2005
Fifth impression 2005
Reprinted 2006 (thrice), 2007, 2008 (twice), 2009

ISBN 978-981-01-8510-7

Printed in Singapore by Times Printers, www.timesprinters.com

ACKNOWLEDGEMENTS

Our special thanks to Richard Askey, Professor of Mathematics (University of Wisconsin, Madison), Yoram Sagher, Professor of Mathematics (University of Illinois, Chicago), and Madge Goldman, President (Gabriella and Paul Rosenbaum Foundation), for their indispensable advice and suggestions in the production of Primary Mathematics (U.S. Edition).

PREFACE

Primary Mathematics (U.S. Edition) comprises textbooks and workbooks. The main feature of this package is the use of the **Concrete ➡ Pictorial ➡ Abstract** approach. The students are provided with the necessary learning experiences beginning with the concrete and pictorial stages, followed by the abstract stage to enable them to learn mathematics meaningfully. This package encourages active thinking processes, communication of mathematical ideas and problem solving.

The textbook comprises 6 units. Each unit is divided into parts: ❶, ❷, . . . Each part starts with a meaningful situation for communication and is followed by specific learning tasks numbered 1, 2, . . . The textbook is accompanied by a workbook. The sign Workbook Exercise is used to link the textbook to the workbook exercises.

Practice exercises are designed to provide the students with further practice after they have done the relevant workbook exercises. Review exercises are provided for cumulative reviews of concepts and skills. All the practice exercises and review exercises are optional exercises.

The color patch ■ is used to invite active participation from the students and to facilitate oral discussion. The students are advised not to write on the color patches.

CONTENTS

1 Whole Numbers

1 Place Values 6
2 Millions 8
PRACTICE 1A 10
3 Approximation and Estimation 11
PRACTICE 1B 14
4 Multiplying by Tens, Hundreds or Thousands 15
5 Dividing by Tens, Hundreds or Thousands 17
6 Order of Operations 19
PRACTICE 1C 21
7 Word Problems 22
PRACTICE 1D 25

2 Multiplication and Division by a 2-digit Whole Number

1 Multiplication 26
2 Division 28
PRACTICE 2A 32

3 Fractions

1 Fraction and Division 33
PRACTICE 3A 36
2 Addition and Subtraction of Unlike Fractions 37
PRACTICE 3B 40
3 Addition and Subtraction of Mixed Numbers 41
PRACTICE 3C 43
4 Product of a Fraction and a Whole Number 44
PRACTICE 3D 48
5 Product of Fractions 49
PRACTICE 3E 52
6 Dividing a Fraction by a Whole Number 53
PRACTICE 3F 55
7 Word Problems 56
PRACTICE 3G 60

REVIEW A **61**

4 **Area of Triangle**
1 Finding the Area of a Triangle 65
PRACTICE 4A 70

5 **Ratio**
1 Finding Ratio 71
2 Equivalent Ratios 75
PRACTICE 5A 79
3 Comparing Three Quantities 80
PRACTICE 5B 82

6 **Angles**
1 Measuring Angles 83
2 Finding Unknown Angles 85

REVIEW B 89

REVIEW C 93

15

1 Whole Numbers

1 Place Values

This block is made up of unit cubes.
How many unit cubes are there?

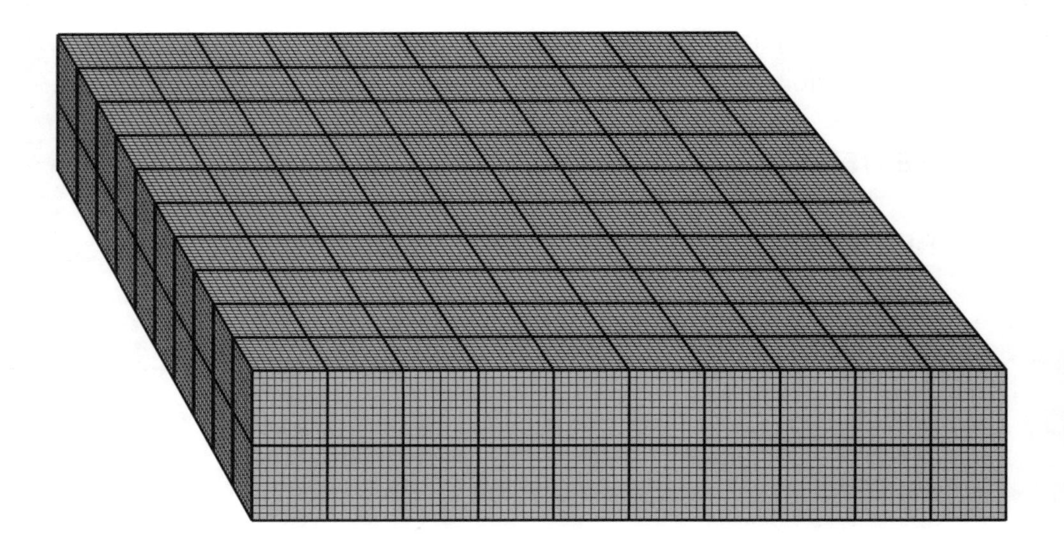

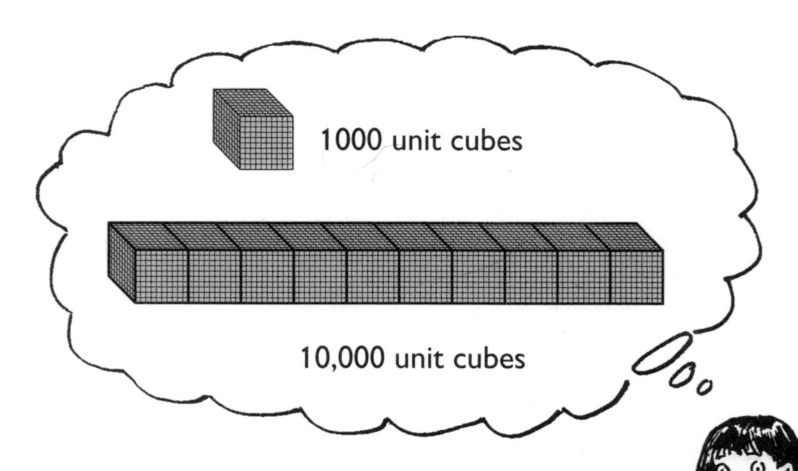

200,000

two hundred thousand

1. A library has a collection of 124,936 books.

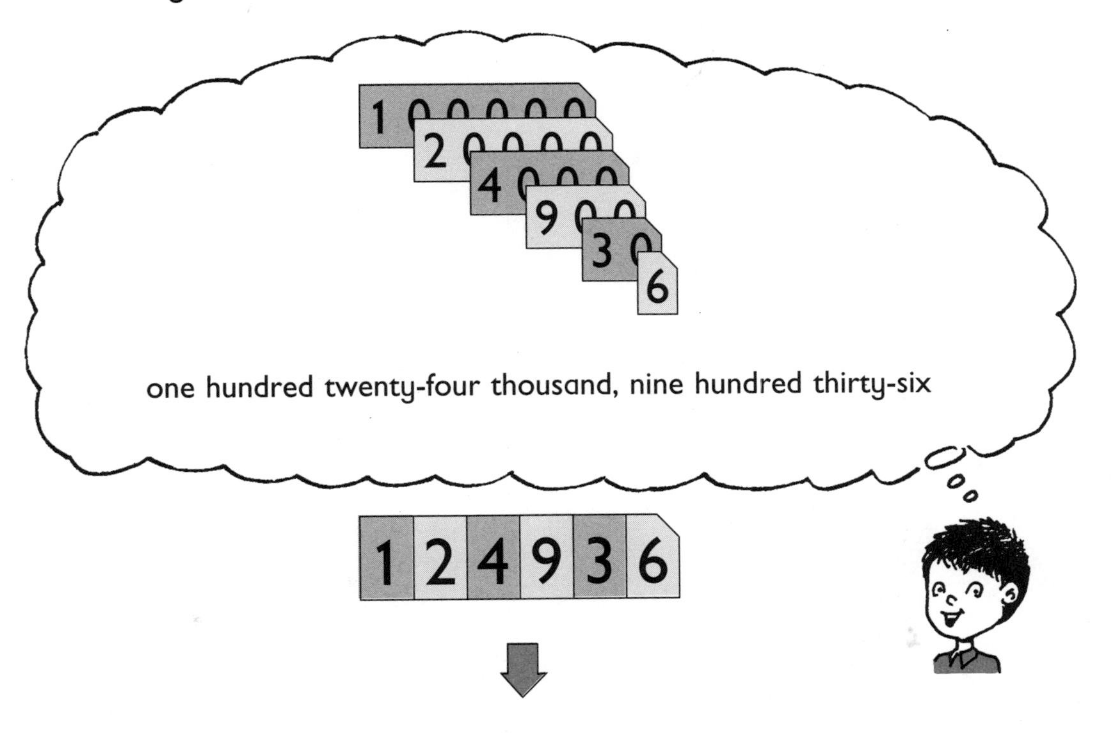

Hundred thousands	Ten thousands	Thousands	Hundreds	Tens	Ones
1	2	4	9	3	6

(a) In 124,936, the digit 2 is in the ten thousands place.

Its value is ■.

(b) The digit 1 is in the hundred thousands place.
Its value is ■.

2. Write the following in words.

(a) 435,672 (b) 500,500 (c) 404,040
(d) 345,713 (e) 700,370 (f) 311,012
(g) 840,382 (h) 600,005 (i) 999,999

3. Write the following in figures.

(a) Four hundred one thousand, sixty-two
(b) Nine hundred seventy thousand, five hundred five
(c) Seven hundred thousand, nine

Workbook Exercise 1

2 Millions

The selling price of the house is $2 **million**.
How many one-thousand-dollar notes do you need to buy the house?

1. (a) According to the 1980 census, the population of Singapore was about 2,414,000.

In 2,414,000, the digit ▇ is in the millions place.

(b) According to the 1990 census, the population of Singapore has exceeded 3,000,000.

In 3,000,000, the digit 3 is in the ▇ place.

2. Write the following in words.
   (a) 5,000,000
   (b) 4,126,000
   (c) 3,690,000
   (d) 6,800,000

3. Write the following in figures.
   (a) Six million
   (b) Seven million, three thousand
   (c) Eight million
   (d) Nine million, twenty-three thousand

Workbook Exercise 2

PRACTICE 1A

1. Write the following in figures.
   (a) Eleven thousand, twelve
   (b) One hundred fifteen thousand, six hundred
   (c) Seven hundred thousand, thirteen
   (d) Eight hundred eighty thousand, five
   (e) Five million
   (f) Four million, two hundred thousand
   (g) Ten million
   (h) Eight million, eight thousand

2. Write the following in words.
   (a) 207,306 (b) 560,003 (c) 700,000
   (d) 3,450,000 (e) 6,020,000 (f) 4,003,000

3. What is the value of the digit 8 in each of the following?
   (a) 72,**8**45 (b) **8**0,375 (c) 901,9**8**2
   (d) **8**10,034 (e) 9,64**8**,000 (f) **8**,162,000

4. What are the missing numbers?
   (a) 16,500 = 10,000 + ■ + 500
   (b) 225,430 = ■ + 20,000 + 5000 + 400 + 30
   (c) 100,000 + 80,000 + 4000 + 900 = ■
   (d) 7,000,000 + 600,000 + 9000 = ■
   (e) 9,000,000 + 20,000 + 1000 = ■
   (f) 8,532,000 = 8,000,000 + 500,000 + ■ + 2000

5. Complete the following number patterns.
   (a) 42,668, 43,668, ■, ■, 46,668
   (b) 70,500, 71,500, 72,500, ■, ■
   (c) 83,002, 93,002, ■, ■, 123,002
   (d) 5,632,000, 5,642,000, ■, ■, 5,672,000
   (e) 9,742,000, 8,742,000, ■, 6,742,000, ■

6. Arrange the numbers in increasing order.
   (a) 53,760, 53,670, 56,370, 53,607
   (b) 324,468, 342,468, 324,648, 342,486
   (c) 2,537,000, 2,357,000, 3,257,000, 425,700

3 Approximation and Estimation

4865 people watched a badminton match.

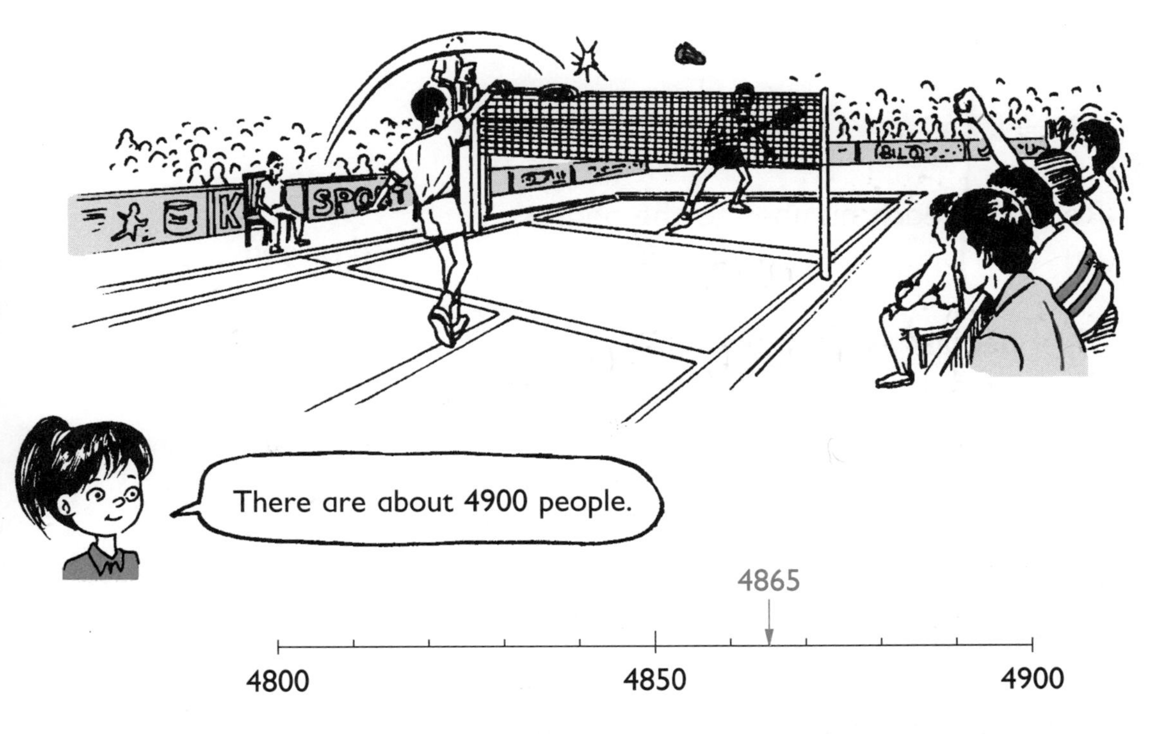

There are about 4900 people.

4865

4800 4850 4900

Sally rounds off 4865 **to the nearest hundred**.

4865 ≈ 4900

4865 is **approximately** 4900.

There are about 5000 people.

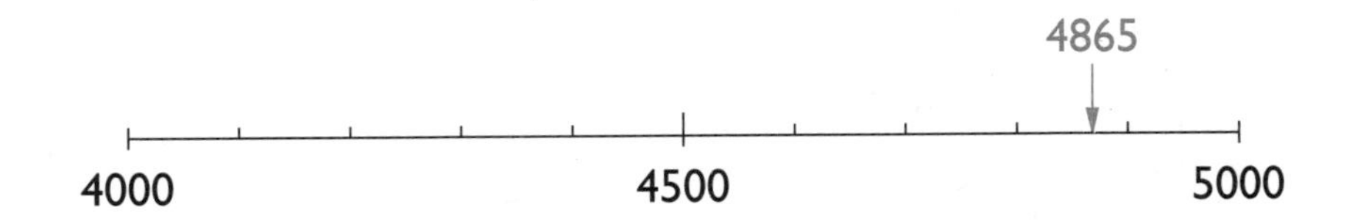

Jenny rounds off 4865 **to the nearest thousand**.

4865 ≈ 5000

4865 is **approximately** 5000.

1. There are 487 pages in a book.
   Round off the number of pages to the nearest ten.

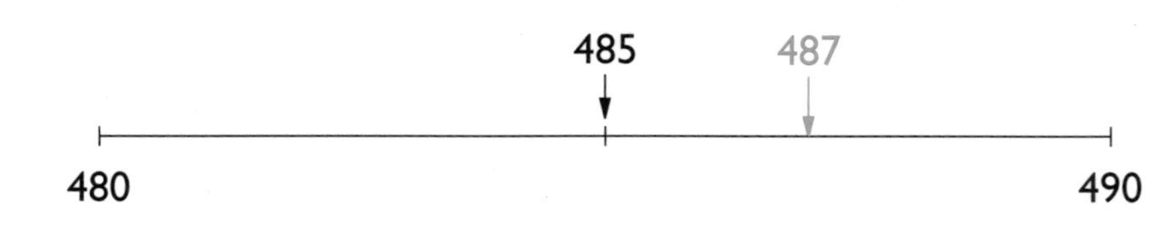

487 ≈ ■

2. Round off each number to the nearest 10.
   (a) 604 (b) 795 (c) 999

3. 5714 people visited a book fair.
   Round off the number of visitors to the nearest hundred.

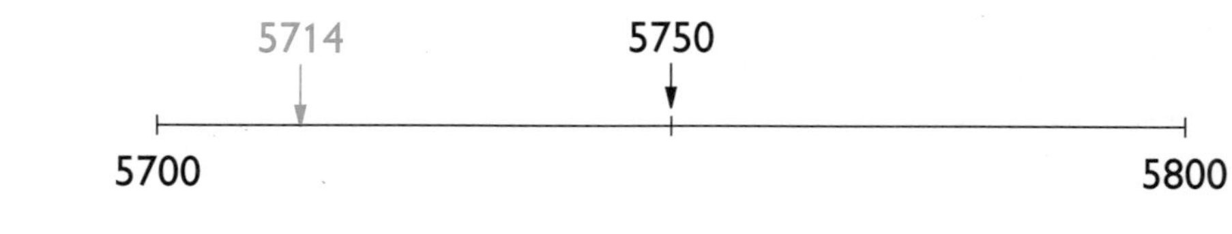

5714 ≈ ■

4. Round off each number to the nearest 100.
   (a) 3650 (b) 6047 (c) 4995

5. Round off 16,500 to the nearest thousand.

16,500 is halfway between 16,000 and 17,000.
We take 17,000 as the nearest 1000.

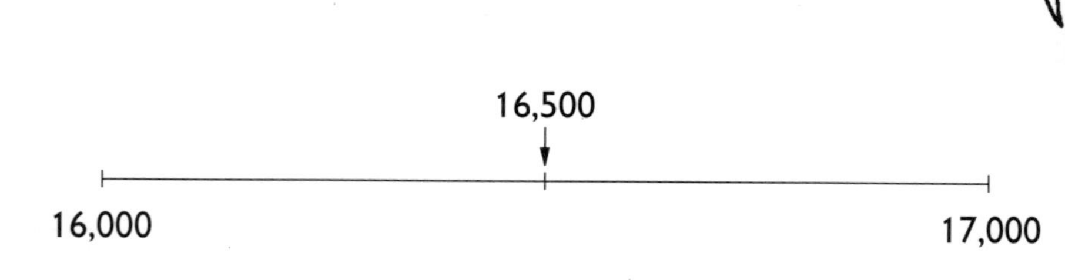

16,500 ≈ ■

6. Round off each number to the nearest 1000.
   (a) 23,490 (b) 54,550 (c) 39,900

Workbook Exercise 3

To round off a number to the nearest thousand, we look at the digit in the hundreds place. If it is 5 or greater than 5, we round up; if it is smaller than 5, we round down.

7. Round off each number to the nearest 1000.
   (a) 49,287 $\approx$ 49,000
   (b) 73,501 $\approx$ $\square$
   (c) 804,390 $\approx$ $\square$
   (d) 129,500 $\approx$ $\square$

8. Find the value of 1800 $\div$ 3.

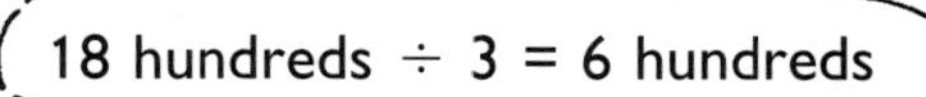

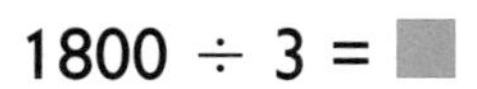

1800 $\div$ 3 = $\square$

9. Find the value of
   (a) 27,000 + 6000
   (b) 45,000 – 8000
   (c) 7000 $\times$ 4
   (d) 3500 $\div$ 5

10. Estimate the value of 2934 $\times$ 6.

2934 $\times$ 6 $\approx$ 3000 $\times$ 6
= $\square$

11. Estimate the value of 5423 $\div$ 8.

5423 $\div$ 8 $\approx$ 5600 $\div$ 8
= $\square$

12. Estimate the value of
   (a) 6390 + 5992
   (b) 78,123 + 8969
   (c) 8307 – 4265
   (d) 45,627 – 7324
   (e) 3806 $\times$ 9
   (f) 9794 $\times$ 5
   (g) 4785 $\div$ 6
   (h) 3782 $\div$ 4

Workbook Exercise 4

PRACTICE 1B

1. Round off each number to the nearest 10.
   (a) 72 (b) 655 (c) 1289

2. Round off each number to the nearest 100.
   (a) 342 (b) 1259 (c) 20,753

3. Round off each number to the nearest 1000.
   (a) 6850 (b) 10,500 (c) 125,498

4. David bought a television set for $849.
   Round off this amount to the nearest hundred dollars.

5. Mr. Ray bought a car for $69,500.
   Round off this amount to the nearest thousand dollars.

6. A spaceship traveled 999,540 km.
   Round off this distance to the nearest 1000 km.

7. This table shows the number of people living in three towns.

   (a) Round off the number of people in each town to the nearest 1000.

   (b) Use your answers in part (a) to estimate the total number of people in the 3 towns.

Number of people
Town A : 179,920
Town B : 176,392
Town C : 170,500

8. Round each number to the nearest 1000.
   Then estimate the value of
   (a) 32,370 + 4959 (b) 24,890 + 5016
   (c) 48,207 – 9864 (d) 54,500 – 6892

9. Estimate the value of
   (a) 8659×4 (b) 6023×9
   (c) $7080 \div 8$ (d) $4378 \div 7$

4 Multiplying by Tens, Hundreds or Thousands

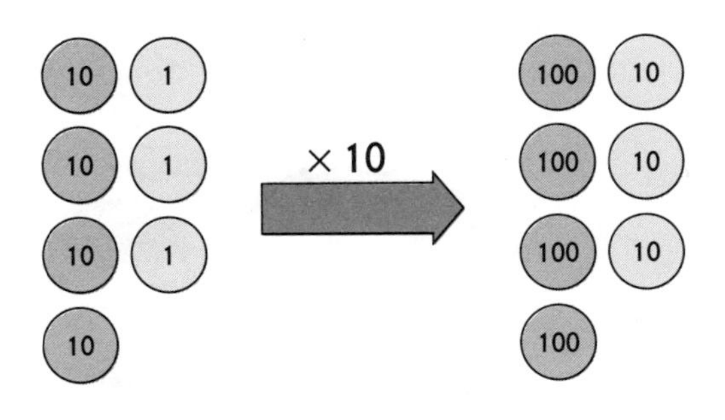

$43 \times 10 = 430$

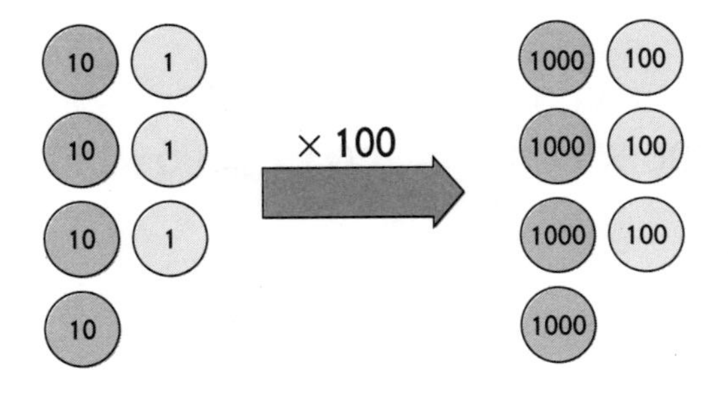

$43 \times 100 = 4300$

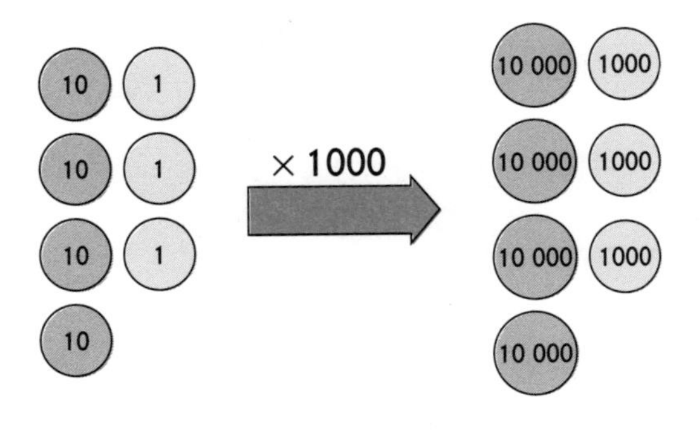

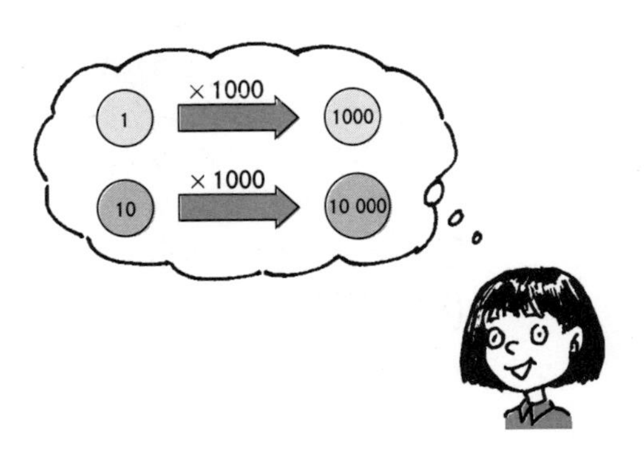

$43 \times 1000 = 43{,}000$

1. Multiply.
(a) 328×10 (b) 100×536 (c) 63×1000

2. Multiply 16 by 70.

$16 \times 70 = 16 \times 7 \times 10$

$= 112 \times 10$

$= 1120$

3. Multiply 48 by 3.
Then find the value of
(a) 48×30 (b) 48×300 (c) 48×3000

4. Multiply 450 by 6.
Then find the value of
(a) 450×60 (b) 450×600 (c) 450×6000

5. Multiply.
(a) 200×500 (b) 600×900 (c) 800×6000
(d) 500×2000 (e) 4000×600 (f) 2000×5000

6. Estimate the value of 702×19.

$702 \times 19 \approx 700 \times 20$

$= \blacksquare$

7. Mrs. Bates needs 543 costumes for the students to take part in a parade. Each costume costs \$35. Give a quick estimate of the total cost of the costumes.

$35 \times 543 \approx 40 \times 500$
$= 20{,}000$

The total cost is about \$20,**000**.

8. Estimate the value of
(a) 529×34 (b) 75×386 (c) 7804×59

Workbook Exercise 5

5 Dividing by Tens, Hundreds or Thousands

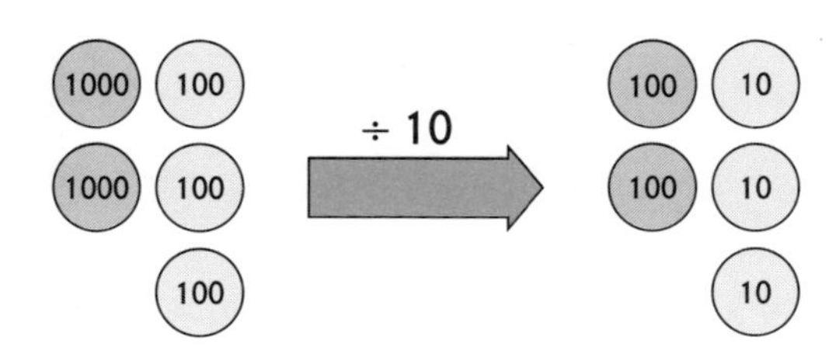

$2300 \div 10 = 230$

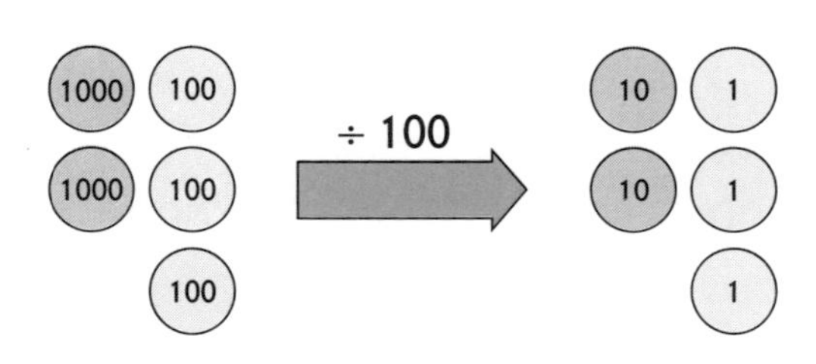

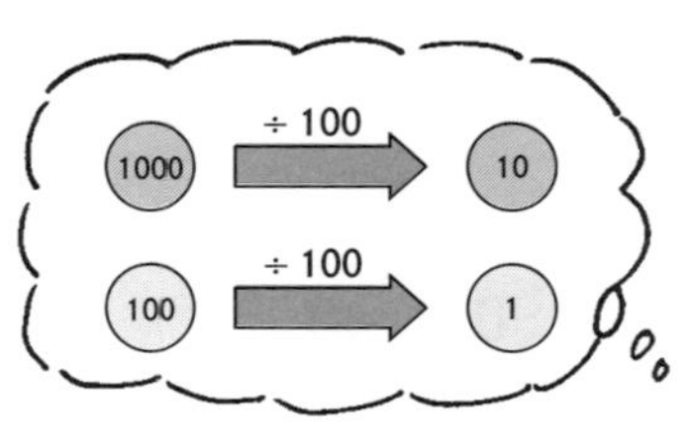

$2300 \div 100 = 23$

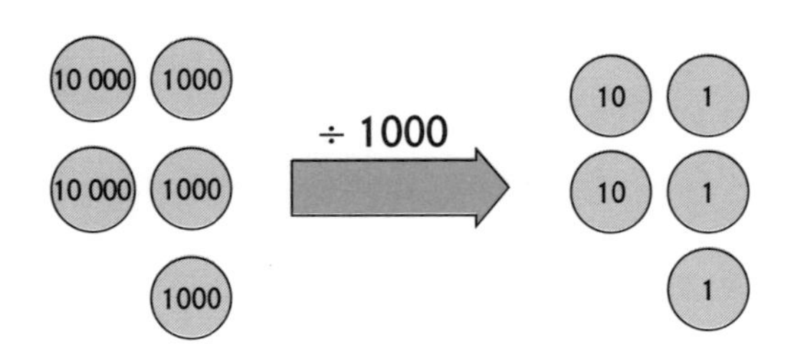

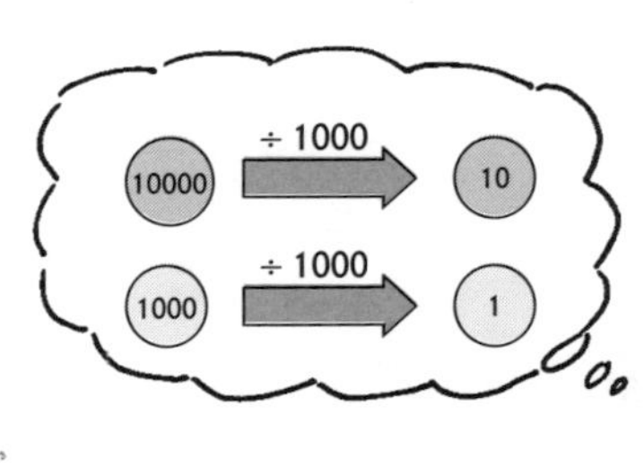

$23{,}000 \div 1000 = 23$

1. Divide.

(a) $520 \div 10$ (b) $7400 \div 100$ (c) $40,000 \div 1000$

2. (a) Divide 15,000 by 30.

$$15,000 \div 30 = 15,000 \div 10 \div 3$$
$$= 1500 \div 3$$
$$= 500$$

(b) Divide 15,000 by 300.

$$15,000 \div 300 = 15,000 \div 100 \div 3$$
$$= 150 \div 3$$
$$= 50$$

(c) Divide 15,000 by 3000.

$$15,000 \div 3000 = 15,000 \div 1000 \div 3$$
$$= 15 \div 3$$
$$= 5$$

3. Divide.

(a) $280 \div 40$ (b) $64,000 \div 800$ (c) $200,000 \div 5000$

4. Estimate the value of $2992 \div 38$.

$$2992 \div 38 \approx 2800 \div 40$$
$$= \blacksquare$$

5. Maria paid \$959 for 33 copies of a software. Give a quick estimate of the cost per copy.

$$959 \div 33 \approx 900 \div 30$$
$$= 30$$

The cost per copy was about \$30.

6. Estimate the value of

(a) $6398 \div 81$ (b) $2205 \div 34$ (c) $638 \div 67$

Workbook Exercise 6

6 Order of Operations

Matthew arranges his stamps on two pages of his stamp album like this:

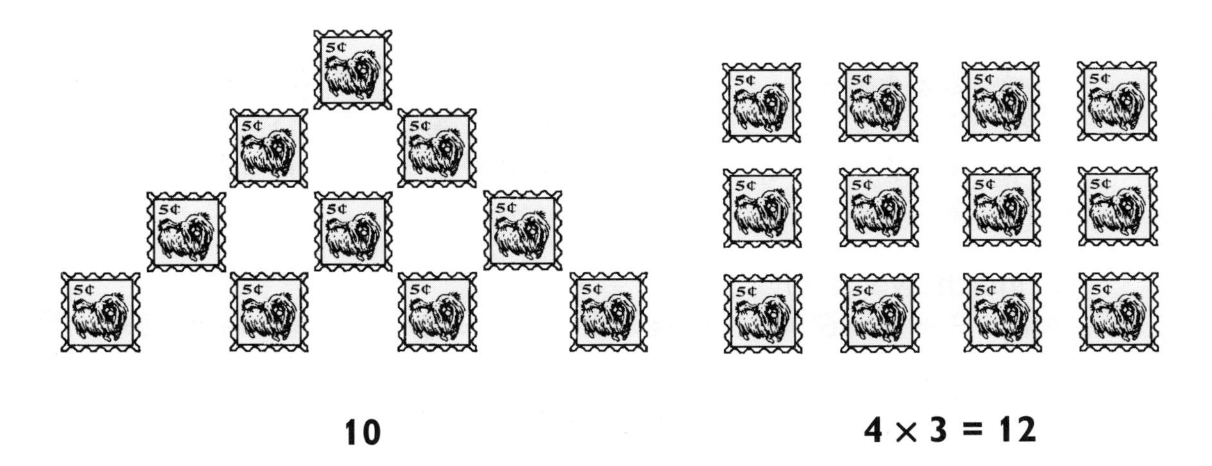

Then he finds the total number of stamps.

Do multiplication first.

$$10 + (4 \times 3) = 10 + 12$$
$$= 22$$

There are 22 stamps altogether.

Order of Operations:

Do multiplication or division from left to right, then addition or subtraction from left to right.

1. Find the value of

(a) $12 + 8 - 10$ (b) $60 - 12 - 24$ (c) $31 - 19 + 11$
(d) $43 + 16 - 27$ (e) $64 + 26 + 57$ (f) $90 - 12 + 21$
(g) $55 + 69 - 25$ (h) $111 - 89 - 11$ (i) $58 - 25 + 42$

2. Find the value of

(a) $2 \times 4 \times 8$ (b) $60 \div 4 \div 3$ (c) $54 \div 6 \times 3$
(d) $9 \times 8 \times 6$ (e) $72 \div 6 \div 4$ (f) $4 \times 24 \div 8$
(g) $4 \times 7 \times 25$ (h) $64 \div 8 \div 8$ (i) $9 \times 81 \div 9$

3. Find the value of

(a) $9 + 3 \times 6$ (b) $27 - 12 \div 3$ (c) $4 + 15 \times 12$
(d) $80 - 5 \times 10$ (e) $54 - 48 \div 6$ (f) $9 + 81 \div 9$
(g) $56 - 8 \times 5 + 4$ (h) $70 + 80 \div 5 \times 4$ (i) $96 \div 8 - 6 \times 2$
(j) $6 + 54 \div 9 \times 2$ (k) $49 - 45 \div 5 \times 3$ (l) $62 + 42 \div 7 - 6$

Workbook Exercise 7

4. Find the value of $27 - 2 \times (3 + 5)$.

$$27 - 2 \times (\mathbf{3 + 5})$$
$$= 27 - 2 \times \mathbf{8}$$
$$= \blacksquare$$

Do what is in the **parentheses** first.

5. Find the value of

(a) $76 + (36 + 164)$ (b) $200 - (87 - 13)$ (c) $99 - (87 + 12)$
(d) $18 \times (5 \times 2)$ (e) $490 \div (7 \times 7)$ (f) $153 \times (27 \div 9)$

6. Find the value of

(a) $60 \div (4 + 8)$ (b) $20 - 2 \times (18 \div 6)$
(c) $25 + (5 + 7) \div 3$ (d) $(22 + 10) \div 8 \times 5$
(e) $(50 - 42) \div 2 \times 7$ (f) $100 \div 10 \times (4 + 6)$

Workbook Exercise 8

PRACTICE 1C

1. Multiply.
   (a) 238×10 (b) 700×100 (c) 37×1000
   (d) 10×400 (e) 100×280 (f) 1000×520

2. Multiply 56 by 7.
   Then find the value of
   (a) 56×70 (b) 56×700 (c) 56×7000

3. Multiply 75 by 9.
   Then find the value of
   (a) 75×90 (b) 75×900 (c) 75×9000

4. Divide 72 by 8.
   Then find the value of
   (a) $720{,}000 \div 80$ (b) $720{,}000 \div 800$ (c) $720{,}000 \div 8000$

5. Divide 900 by 6.
   Then find the value of
   (a) $90{,}000 \div 60$ (b) $90{,}000 \div 600$ (c) $90{,}000 \div 6000$

6. Divide.
   (a) $360 \div 90$ (b) $7600 \div 40$ (c) $90{,}600 \div 600$
   (d) $4080 \div 80$ (e) $350{,}000 \div 500$ (f) $412{,}000 \div 4000$

7. Find the value of
   (a) $(48 - 17) + 25$ (b) $6 \times 5 \times 10$
   (c) $81 \div 9 \div 3$ (d) $50 \div 5 + 5$
   (e) $64 - 3 \times 9$ (f) $72 - 36 \div 9$
   (g) $27 + 15 \div 3 \times 2$ (h) $40 \div 2 - 2 \times 5$
   (i) $10 + 24 \div 8 + 8$ (j) $(38 - 17) \div 3 \times 10$
   (k) $35 \div (10 - 3) \times 10$ (l) $(13 + 7) \div (9 - 4)$

8. Find the value of
   (a) $372 - (45 - 29)$ (b) $372 - 45 + 29$
   (c) $372 - 45 - 29$ (d) $372 - (45 + 29)$
   (e) $128 \div 4 \div 2$ (f) $128 \div (4 \times 2)$
   (g) $128 \div 4 \times 2$ (h) $128 \div (4 \div 2)$

Word Problems

Alicia bought 420 mangoes for $378. She packed the mangoes in bags of 4 mangoes each and sold all the mangoes at $6 per bag. How much money did she make?

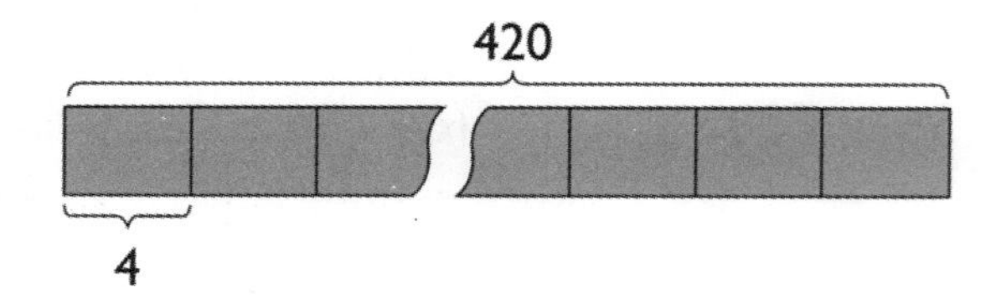

4 mangoes in 1 bag

420 mangoes in ■ bags.

$$420 \div 4 = 105$$

There were 105 bags of mangoes.

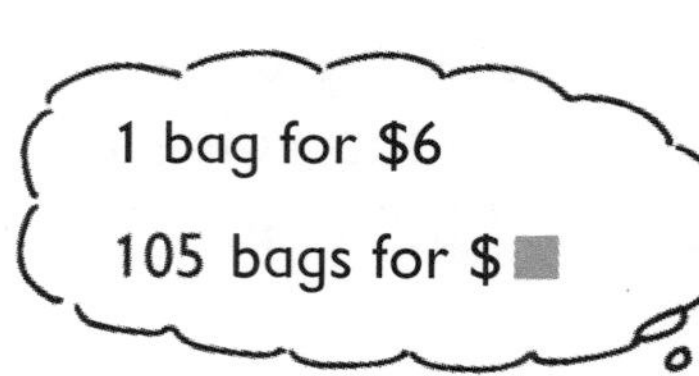

$$\$6 \times 105 = \$630$$

Alicia sold the mangoes for $630.

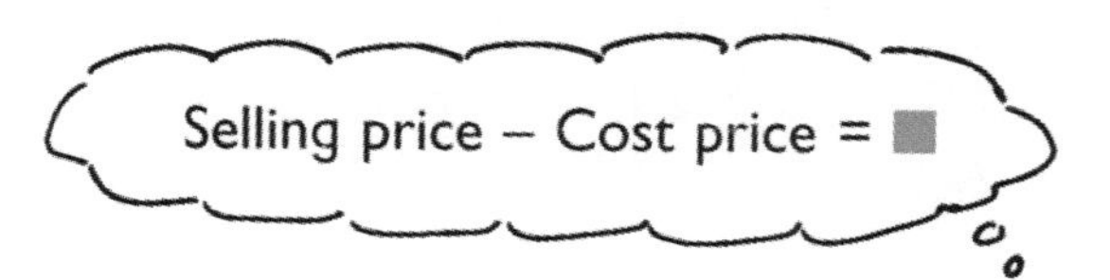

$$\$630 - \$378 = \$■$$

Alicia made $■.

1. Ryan and Juan shared \$410 between them. Ryan received \$100 more than Juan. How much money did Juan receive?

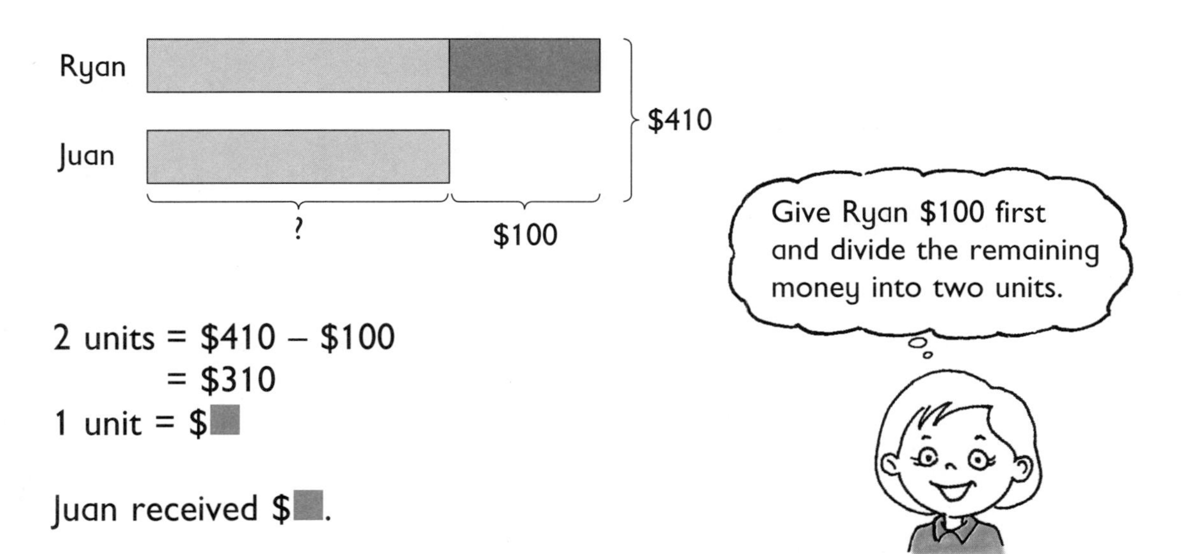

2 units = \$410 – \$100
= \$310
1 unit = \$▮

Juan received \$▮.

2. Peter collected a total of 1170 stamps. He collected 4 times as many U.S. stamps as foreign stamps. How many U.S. stamps did he collect?

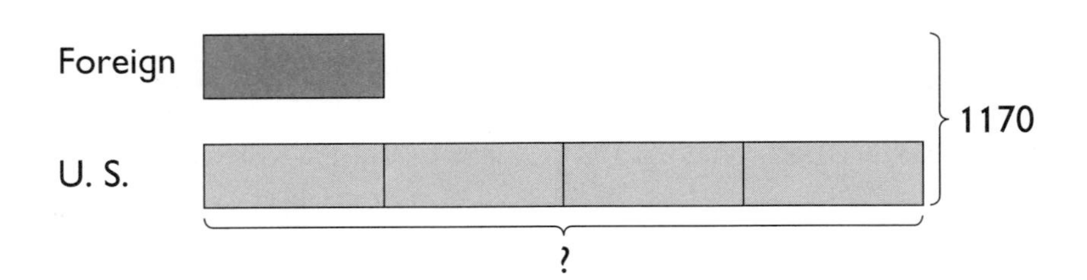

Workbook Exercise 9

3. Mr. Given bought 2 similar T-shirts and a belt. He paid \$50 to the cashier and received \$3 change. If the belt cost \$29, find the cost of each T-shirt.

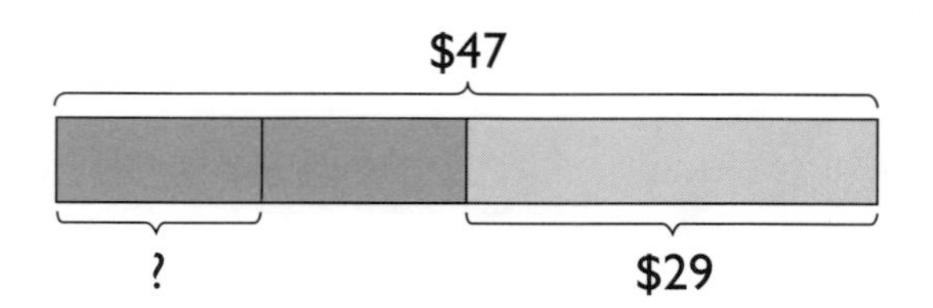

$\$50 - \$3 = \$47$

Mr. Given spent \$47.

$\$47 - \$29 = \$18$

The total cost of 2 T-shirts and 1 belt is \$47.

The T-shirts cost \$18.

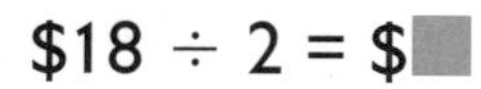

$\$18 \div 2 = \$$■

The cost of each T-shirt was \$■.

4. Henry bought a compact disc and 3 videotapes. The compact disc cost \$16. If a compact disc cost twice as much as a videotape, how much did he spend altogether?

$16

CD

Tape

?

$\$16 \div 2 = \$8$

A videotape cost \$8.

$\$8 \times 3 = \$24$

The cost of 3 videotapes was \$24.

He bought 3 videotapes and 1 compact disc.

$\$24 + \$16 = \$$■

He spent \$■ altogether.

Workbook Exercise 10

PRACTICE 1D

1. John is 15 kg heavier than Peter. Their total weight is 127 kg. Find John's weight.

2. There are 3 times as many boys as girls. If there are 24 more boys than girls, how many children are there altogether?

3. The total weight of Peter, David and Henry is 123 kg. Peter is 15 kg heavier than David. David is 3 kg lighter than Henry. Find Henry's weight.

4. Pablo has $180 and Ryan has $150. How much money must Pablo give Ryan so that they each will have an equal amount of money?

5. Matthew has twice as many stickers as David. How many stickers must Matthew give David so that they each will have 120 stickers?

6. Peter has twice as many stickers as Joe. Joe has 40 more stickers than Emily. They have 300 stickers altogether. How many stickers does Peter have?

7. At a book fair, Joe bought 24 books at 3 for $5 and had $2 left. How much money did he have at first?

8. Ryan bought 3 books and a magazine. He paid $30 to the cashier and received $5 change. If the magazine cost twice as much as each book, find the cost of the magazine.

9. Harry bought 155 oranges for $35. He found that 15 of them were rotten. He sold all the remaining oranges at 7 for $2. How much money did he make?

10. John and Paul spent $45 altogether. John and Henry spent $65 altogether. If Henry spent 3 times as much as Paul, how much did John spend?

2 Multiplication and Division by a 2-digit Whole Number

1 Multiplication

(a) Multiply 78 by 30.

Method 1:

$78 \times 30 = 78 \times 3 \times 10$

$= 234 \times 10$

$= 2340$

Method 2:

$$\begin{array}{r} 78 \\ \times\ 30 \\ \hline 2340 \end{array}$$

(b) Multiply 650 by 40.

$$\begin{array}{r} 650 \\ \times\ 40 \\ \hline 26000 \\ \hline \end{array}$$

1. Multiply.

(a)
$$\begin{array}{r} 53 \\ \times\ 60 \\ \hline \blacksquare \end{array}$$

(b)
$$\begin{array}{r} 247 \\ \times\ 80 \\ \hline \blacksquare \end{array}$$

2. Multiply.

(a) 58×80 (b) 46×50 (c) 27×90

(d) 207×60 (e) 739×40 (f) 641×70

3. Multiply.

(a)
$$\begin{array}{rl} 24 & \\ \times\ 13 & \\ \hline 72 & \leftarrow 24 \times 3 \\ 240 & \leftarrow 24 \times 10 \\ \hline 312 & \end{array}$$

(b)
$$\begin{array}{r} 52 \\ \times\ 47 \\ \hline \blacksquare \end{array}$$

(c)
$$\begin{array}{rl} 325 & \\ \times\ 54 & \\ \hline 1300 & \leftarrow 325 \times 4 \\ 16250 & \leftarrow 325 \times 50 \\ \hline \blacksquare & \end{array}$$

(d)
$$\begin{array}{r} 618 \\ \times\ 72 \\ \hline \blacksquare \end{array}$$

4. Multiply.

(a) 67×44 (b) 53×48 (c) 29×96

(d) 236×82 (e) 457×35 (f) 606×47

5. Multiply.

(a)
$$\begin{array}{r} 4635 \\ \times\ 26 \\ \hline \blacksquare \end{array}$$

(b)
$$\begin{array}{r} 8247 \\ \times\ 38 \\ \hline \blacksquare \end{array}$$

6. Multiply.

(a) 3059×53 (b) 7105×62 (c) 2537×48

(d) 3860×69 (e) 6394×57 (f) 5482×74

Workbook Exercise 11

2 Division

(a) Divide 140 by 20.

Method 1:

$14\mathbf{0} \div 2\mathbf{0} = 7$

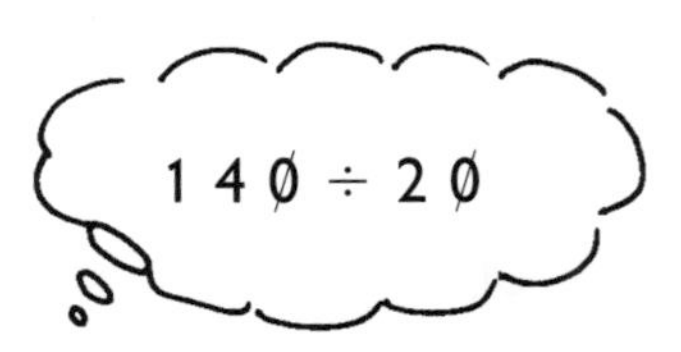

Method 2:

$$\begin{array}{r} \mathbf{7} \\ 20\overline{)140} \\ 140 \\ \hline 0 \end{array}$$

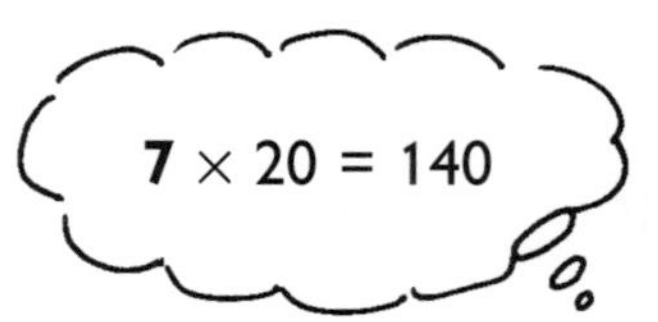

(b) Divide 150 by 20.

$$\begin{array}{r} \mathbf{7} \\ 20\overline{)150} \\ 140 \\ \hline 10 \end{array}$$

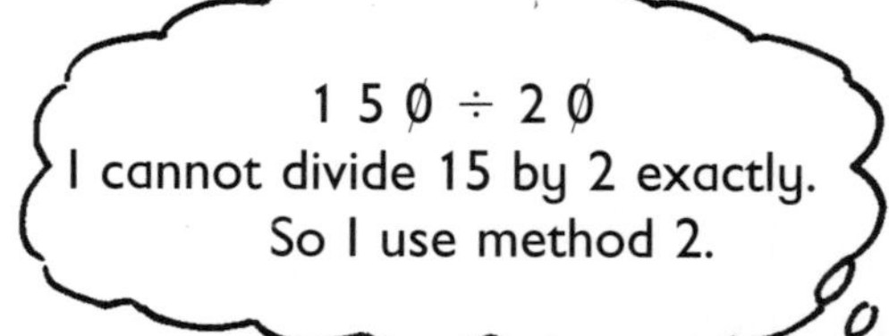

1. Divide.

(a) $30\overline{)70}$ quotient: ▢

(b) $60\overline{)430}$ quotient: ▢

(c) $20\overline{)89}$ quotient: ▢

(d) $70\overline{)625}$ quotient: ▢

2. Divide.

(a) $90 \div 50$ (b) $79 \div 40$ (c) $85 \div 30$

(d) $540 \div 70$ (e) $613 \div 90$ (f) $438 \div 60$

3. Divide 74 by 21.

$$\begin{array}{r} 3 \\ 21\overline{)74} \\ 63 \\ \hline 11 \end{array}$$

4. Divide 256 by 47.

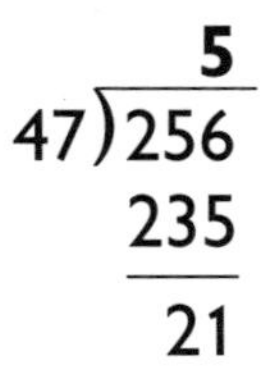

$$\begin{array}{r} 5 \\ 47\overline{)256} \\ 235 \\ \hline 21 \end{array}$$

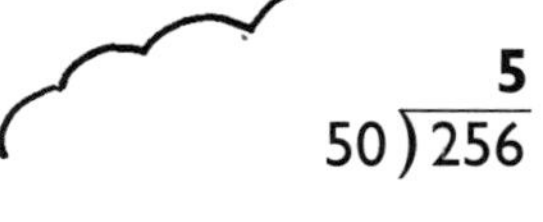

5. Divide.

(a) $63 \div 17$ (b) $48 \div 23$ (c) $85 \div 38$

(d) $76 \div 34$ (e) $94 \div 43$ (f) $57 \div 29$

(g) $149 \div 67$ (h) $509 \div 84$ (i) $756 \div 95$

(j) $668 \div 72$ (k) $279 \div 56$ (l) $183 \div 44$

6. Divide 89 by 24.

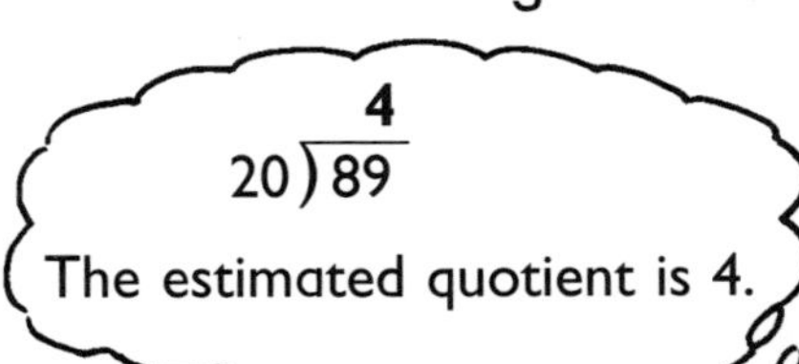

$$\begin{array}{r} 4 \\ 24\overline{)89} \\ 96 \\ \hline \end{array}$$

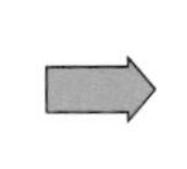

$$\begin{array}{r} 3 \\ 24\overline{)89} \\ 72 \\ \hline 17 \end{array}$$

7. Divide 78 by 26.

$$\begin{array}{r} 2 \\ 26\overline{)78} \\ 52 \\ \hline 26 \end{array} \quad \Rightarrow \quad \begin{array}{r} 3 \\ 26\overline{)78} \\ 78 \\ \hline 0 \end{array}$$

The estimated quotient is too small. Try 3.

8. Divide.

(a) 68 ÷ 17 (b) 77 ÷ 25 (c) 94 ÷ 33
(d) 83 ÷ 21 (e) 84 ÷ 43 (f) 75 ÷ 15

9. Divide 285 by 33.

$$\begin{array}{r} 9 \\ 33\overline{)285} \\ 297 \end{array} \quad \Rightarrow \quad \begin{array}{r} 8 \\ 33\overline{)285} \\ 264 \\ \hline 21 \end{array}$$

The estimated quotient is too big. Try 8.

10. Divide 473 by 78.

$$\begin{array}{r} 5 \\ 78\overline{)473} \\ 390 \\ \hline 83 \end{array} \quad \Rightarrow \quad \begin{array}{r} 6 \\ 78\overline{)473} \\ 468 \\ \hline 5 \end{array}$$

The estimated quotient is too small. Try 6.

11. Divide.

(a) 207 ÷ 23 (b) 236 ÷ 39 (c) 474 ÷ 79
(d) 572 ÷ 64 (e) 464 ÷ 58 (f) 640 ÷ 93

Workbook Exercise 12

12. Divide 570 by 16.

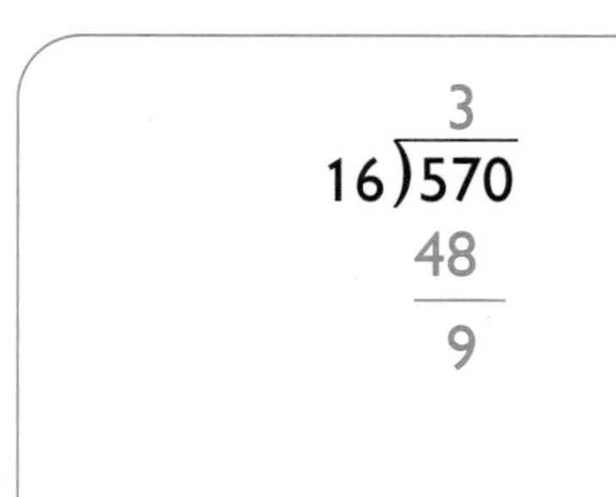

35
16)570
48
90
80
10

Divide 90 by 16.

13. Divide.

(a)
25
34)870
68
190
170
20

(b)
30
28)862
84
22

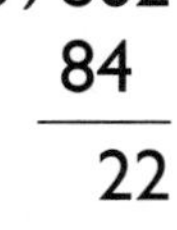

(c) 47)703

(d) 15)612

14. Divide.

(a) $552 \div 24$ (b) $660 \div 29$ (c) $925 \div 46$

(d) $399 \div 31$ (e) $708 \div 67$ (f) $374 \div 18$

15. Divide.

(a)
234
28)6552
56
95
84
112
112
0

(b)
83
52)4328
416
168
156
12

(c) 64)6820

(d) 45)3185

16. Divide.

(a) $6692 \div 28$ (b) $2409 \div 18$ (c) $1495 \div 45$

(d) $6008 \div 56$ (e) $1054 \div 37$ (f) $9864 \div 29$

Workbook Exercise 13

PRACTICE 2A

Multiply.

	(a)	(b)	(c)
1.	407×84	690×49	941×73
2.	5395×51	7404×85	3092×63

Divide.

	(a)	(b)	(c)
3.	$89 \div 24$	$92 \div 33$	$56 \div 18$
4.	$848 \div 16$	$403 \div 67$	$505 \div 53$
5.	$722 \div 38$	$895 \div 23$	$999 \div 42$
6.	$7684 \div 78$	$1340 \div 23$	$9670 \div 54$

7. A baker uses 12 eggs to bake a cake.
   How many eggs does he need if he wants to bake 36 cakes?

8. Mr. Hill has to drive to a city which is 240 km from Portland.
   If his car can travel 15 km on 1 liter of gas, how many liters of gas does he need for the trip?

9. 1064 balloons were shared equally among 38 students. How many balloons did each student receive?

10. Mrs. Garcia sold 96 tarts at a food fair. The tarts were sold in boxes of 12 tarts each. She sold all the tarts at $7 per box. How much money did she receive?

11. Mr. Kent buys a car and pays by installments. Each installment is $827. If he still has to pay $280 after paying 72 installments, how much does the car cost?

12. Miss Lee sold 2034 concert tickets at $16 per ticket. She also sold 840 programs at $3 each. How much money did she collect altogether?

13. 70 students were divided into 14 teams. In each team there were 2 girls. How many boys were there altogether?

14. Mrs. Ward baked 840 cookies. She sold them in packets of 24 cookies each. How much money did she receive if the selling price per packet was $3?

3 Fractions

1 Fraction and Division

4 children share 3 pancakes equally.
Each child receives 3 quarters.

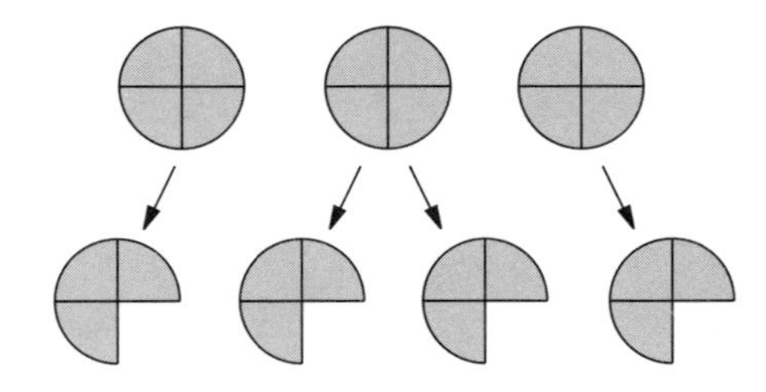

$$3 \div 4 = \frac{3}{4}$$

4 children share 5 pancakes equally.
Each child receives 5 quarters.

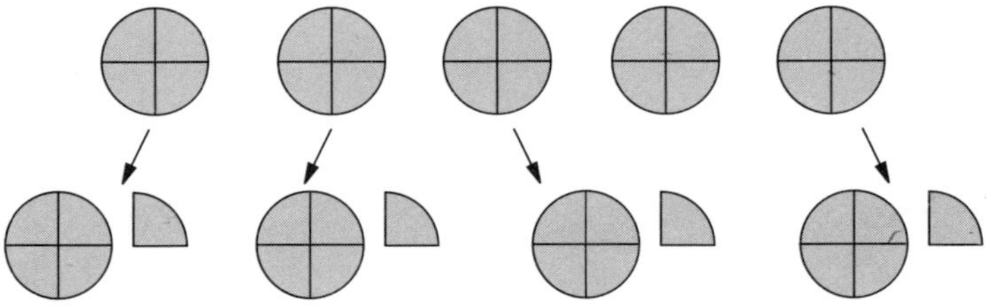

$$5 \div 4 = \frac{5}{4}$$

Here is another way to show that $5 \div 4 = \frac{5}{4}$.

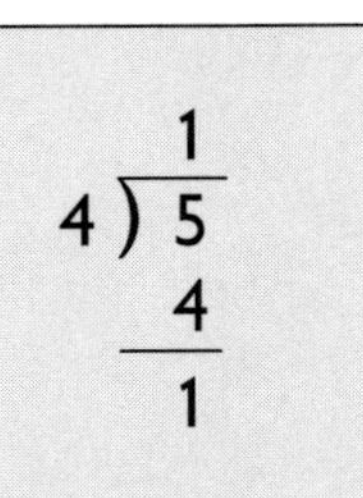

Each child receives 1 pancake first.
Share the remaining pancake.

$1 \div 4 = \frac{1}{4}$

Each child receives 1 and $\frac{1}{4}$ pancakes.

$$\begin{aligned} 5 \div 4 &= 1\tfrac{1}{4} \\ &= \frac{4}{4} + \frac{1}{4} \\ &= \frac{5}{4} \end{aligned}$$

1. Express $\frac{11}{4}$ as a mixed number.

Method 1:

$$\begin{aligned} \frac{11}{4} &= \frac{8}{4} + \frac{3}{4} \\ &= 2\tfrac{3}{4} \end{aligned}$$

Method 2:

$\frac{11}{4} = 11 \div 4 = $ ▇

$$\begin{array}{r} 2 \\ 4 \overline{)\,11} \\ 8 \\ \hline 3 \end{array}$$

2. A bucket contains 8 qt of water. If the water is poured equally into 3 jugs, how much water is there in each jug?

$8 \div 3 = \blacksquare$

$$\begin{array}{r} 2 \\ 3\overline{)\,8} \\ 6 \\ \hline 2 \end{array}$$

There are $\blacksquare$ qt of water in each jug.

3. Find the value of $22 \div 8$.

Method 1:

$$22 \div 8 = 2\frac{6}{8}$$

$$= 2\frac{\blacksquare}{4}$$

$$\begin{array}{r} 2 \\ 8\overline{)\,22} \\ 16 \\ \hline 6 \end{array}$$

Method 2:

$$22 \div 8 = \frac{22}{8}$$

$$= \frac{\blacksquare}{4}$$

$$= \blacksquare$$

4. Find the value of

(a) $7 \div 3$ (b) $14 \div 5$ (c) $21 \div 6$ (d) $77 \div 9$

Workbook Exercise 14

PRACTICE 3A

1. Express each of the following as a whole number or a mixed number in its simplest form.

   (a) $\frac{13}{5}$ (b) $\frac{21}{3}$ (c) $\frac{24}{9}$ (d) $\frac{50}{6}$

2. Express each of the following answers as a mixed number in its simplest form.

   (a) $30 \div 8$ (b) $21 \div 4$ (c) $35 \div 10$ (d) $78 \div 7$

3. Nancy cut a ribbon into 8 equal pieces. If the ribbon was 26 m long, how many meters long was each piece?

4. Mrs. York bought 3 m of cloth. She used the cloth to make 9 pillow cases of the same size. How much cloth in meters did she use for each pillow case?

5. Mary baked 10 cakes of the same size. She divided the cakes into 4 equal shares. How many cakes were there in each share?

6. Peter poured 2 liters of milk equally into 5 jugs. How much milk was there in each jug?

7. A red ribbon 11 m long is 5 times as long as a blue ribbon. How long is the blue ribbon?

8. A box of cookies weighing 4 kg was divided into 6 equal shares. What was the weight of each share in kilograms?

2 Addition and Subtraction of Unlike Fractions

Ann ate $\frac{1}{3}$ of a cake.

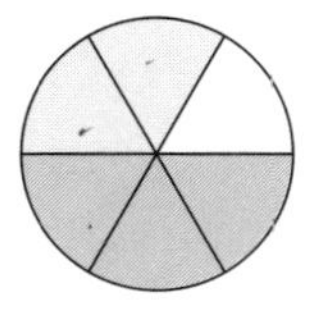
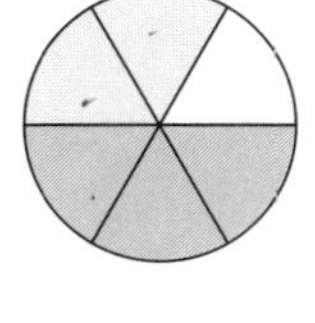

Her brother ate $\frac{1}{2}$ of the same cake.

What fraction of the cake did they eat altogether?

$$\frac{1}{3} + \frac{1}{2} = \frac{2}{6} + \frac{3}{6}$$

$$= \square$$

The cake is divided into 6 equal parts.
Ann ate 2 parts and her brother ate 3 parts.

They ate $\square$ of the cake altogether.

$\frac{1}{3}$ and $\frac{1}{2}$ do not have the same denominator.
They are called **unlike fractions**.

$\frac{2}{6}$ and $\frac{3}{6}$ have the same denominator.
They are called **like fractions**.

We can change unlike fractions to like fractions using equivalent fractions:
$\frac{1}{3}, \frac{2}{6}, \ldots$
$\frac{1}{2}, \frac{3}{6}, \ldots$

1. Add $\frac{3}{8}$ and $\frac{1}{6}$.

$$\frac{3}{8} + \frac{1}{6} = \frac{\square}{24} + \frac{\square}{24}$$
$$= \frac{\square}{24}$$

$\frac{3}{8}, \frac{\square}{16}, \frac{\square}{24}, \ldots$

$\frac{1}{6}, \ldots$

24 is a multiple of 8.
It is also a multiple of 6.

2. Add $\frac{2}{3}$ and $\frac{2}{5}$.

$$\frac{2}{3} + \frac{2}{5} = \frac{\square}{15} + \frac{\square}{15}$$
$$= \frac{\square}{15}$$
$$= \square$$

$\frac{2}{5}, \frac{\square}{10}, \frac{\square}{15}, \ldots$

$\frac{2}{3}, \ldots$

15 is a common multiple of 5 and 3.

3. Add $\frac{7}{10}$ and $\frac{5}{6}$.

$$\frac{7}{10} + \frac{5}{6} = \frac{\square}{30} + \frac{\square}{30}$$
$$= \frac{\square}{30}$$
$$= \frac{\square}{15}$$
$$= \square$$

$\frac{7}{10}, \frac{\square}{20}, \frac{\square}{30}, \ldots$

$\frac{5}{6}, \ldots$

30 is a common multiple of 10 and 6.

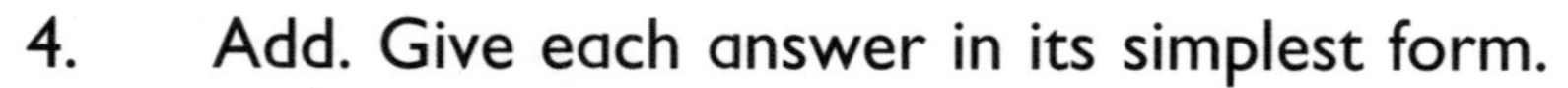

4. Add. Give each answer in its simplest form.

(a) $\frac{7}{9} + \frac{5}{6}$ (b) $\frac{3}{4} + \frac{5}{12}$ (c) $\frac{3}{10} + \frac{5}{6}$

Workbook Exercise 15

5. Subtract $\frac{1}{6}$ from $\frac{7}{8}$.

$\frac{7}{8} - \frac{1}{6} = \frac{\square}{24} - \frac{\square}{24}$

$= \frac{\square}{24}$

$\frac{7}{8}, \frac{\square}{16}, \frac{\square}{24}, \ldots$

$\frac{1}{6}, \ldots$

24 is a common multiple of 8 and 6.

6. Subtract $\frac{1}{10}$ from $\frac{5}{6}$.

$\frac{5}{6} - \frac{1}{10} = \frac{\square}{30} - \frac{\square}{30}$

$= \frac{\square}{30}$

$= \frac{\square}{15}$

$\frac{1}{10}, \frac{\square}{20}, \frac{\square}{30}, \ldots$

$\frac{5}{6}, \ldots$

30 is a common multiple of 10 and 6.

7. Subtract $\frac{5}{6}$ from $1\frac{7}{10}$.

$1\frac{7}{10} - \frac{5}{6} = \frac{\square}{30} - \frac{\square}{30}$

$= \frac{\square}{30} - \frac{\square}{30}$

$= \frac{\square}{15}$

8. Subtract. Give each answer in its simplest form.

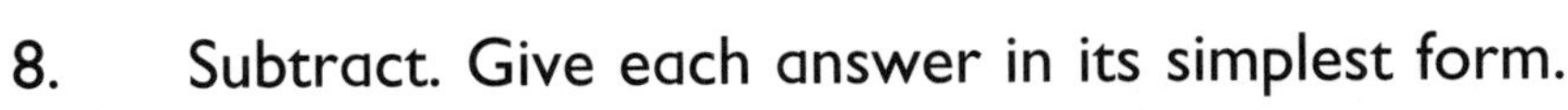

(a) $\frac{5}{6} - \frac{3}{10}$ (b) $1\frac{2}{3} - \frac{11}{12}$ (c) $1\frac{1}{10} - \frac{5}{6}$

Workbook Exercise 16

PRACTICE 3B

Add or subtract. Give each answer in its simplest form.

	(a)	(b)	(c)
1.	$\frac{7}{12} + \frac{5}{6}$	$\frac{9}{10} + \frac{1}{6}$	$\frac{5}{6} + \frac{7}{8}$
2.	$\frac{2}{3} - \frac{5}{12}$	$\frac{5}{6} - \frac{7}{10}$	$\frac{3}{4} - \frac{1}{6}$
3.	$\frac{1}{6} + \frac{3}{10}$	$\frac{2}{3} + \frac{1}{12}$	$\frac{5}{12} + \frac{1}{8}$
4.	$1\frac{3}{8} - \frac{7}{12}$	$1\frac{1}{3} - \frac{7}{10}$	$1\frac{3}{10} - \frac{5}{6}$

5. John mowed $\frac{2}{5}$ of a lawn. His brother mowed $\frac{1}{4}$ of it. What fraction of the lawn did they mow?

6. Samy took $\frac{3}{4}$ hour to travel from home to the zoo. He took $1\frac{1}{4}$ hours to return home. How much longer did he take to return home than to go to the zoo?

7. Mary ate $\frac{1}{8}$ of a cake. Peter ate another $\frac{1}{4}$ of it.
   (a) What fraction of the cake did they eat altogether?
   (b) What fraction of the cake did Peter eat more than Mary?

8. Ali went to a bookshop. He spent $\frac{3}{5}$ of his money on books and $\frac{1}{4}$ of it on a pen.
   (a) What fraction of his money did he spend altogether?
   (b) What fraction of his money did he have left?

3 Addition and Subtraction of Mixed Numbers

$3\frac{5}{8}$ m

$1\frac{7}{12}$ m

(a) Find the total length of $3\frac{5}{8}$ m and $1\frac{7}{12}$ m.

$$3\frac{5}{8} + 1\frac{7}{12} = 4\frac{5}{8} + \frac{7}{12}$$
$$= 4\frac{15}{24} + \frac{14}{24}$$
$$= 4\frac{■}{24}$$
$$= ■$$

The total length is ■ m.

(b) Add $4\frac{7}{12}$ and $1\frac{3}{4}$.

$$4\frac{7}{12} + 1\frac{3}{4} = 5\frac{7}{12} + \frac{3}{4}$$
$$= 5\frac{7}{12} + \frac{9}{12}$$
$$= 5\frac{■}{12}$$
$$= 5\frac{■}{3}$$
$$= ■$$

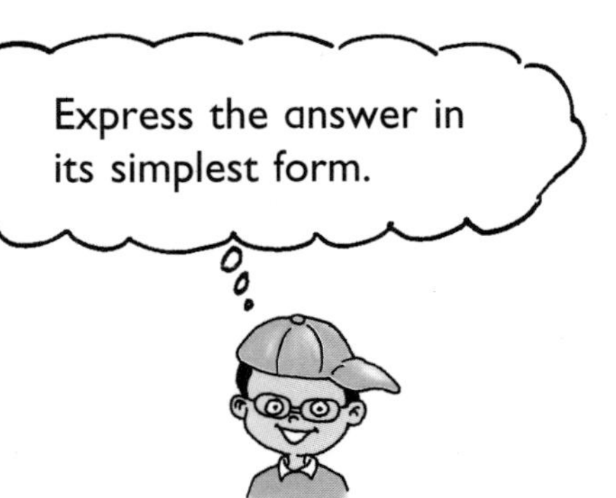

1. Add $3\frac{1}{6}$ and $1\frac{9}{10}$.

$$3\frac{1}{6} + 1\frac{9}{10} = 4\frac{1}{6} + \frac{9}{10}$$

$$= 4\frac{\blacksquare}{30} + \frac{\blacksquare}{30}$$

$$= 4\frac{\blacksquare}{30}$$

$$= \blacksquare$$

Workbook Exercise 17

2. Find the difference in length between $4\frac{3}{4}$ m and $3\frac{7}{12}$ m.

$$4\frac{3}{4} - 3\frac{7}{12} = 1\frac{3}{4} - \frac{7}{12}$$

$$= 1\frac{9}{12} - \frac{7}{12}$$

$$= 1\frac{\blacksquare}{12}$$

$$= \blacksquare$$

The difference in length is $\blacksquare$ m.

3. Subtract.

(a) $3\frac{1}{6} - 1\frac{5}{9} = 2\frac{1}{6} - \frac{5}{9}$

$$= 2\frac{3}{18} - \frac{10}{18}$$

$$= 1\frac{\blacksquare}{18} - \frac{10}{18}$$

$$= \blacksquare$$

(b) $4\frac{1}{6} - 1\frac{3}{10} = 3\frac{1}{6} - \frac{3}{10}$

$$= 3\frac{\blacksquare}{30} - \frac{9}{30}$$

$$= 2\frac{\blacksquare}{30} - \frac{9}{30}$$

$$= 2\frac{\blacksquare}{30} = \blacksquare$$

$$= \blacksquare$$

Workbook Exercise 18

PRACTICE 3C

Add or subtract. Give each answer in its simplest form.

	(a)	(b)	(c)
1.	$2\frac{2}{3} + 1\frac{5}{9}$	$2\frac{1}{8} + 1\frac{5}{6}$	$1\frac{1}{4} + 2\frac{5}{6}$
2.	$3\frac{5}{6} - 1\frac{1}{3}$	$3\frac{4}{5} - 1\frac{3}{10}$	$4\frac{5}{6} - 1\frac{1}{4}$
3.	$3\frac{2}{9} + 1\frac{1}{6}$	$2\frac{5}{6} + 5\frac{1}{2}$	$2\frac{5}{6} + 1\frac{3}{8}$
4.	$4\frac{1}{6} - 1\frac{2}{3}$	$3\frac{1}{6} - 2\frac{1}{10}$	$3\frac{3}{10} - 1\frac{1}{6}$

5. Robert jogged $1\frac{2}{5}$ km. His brother jogged $2\frac{1}{2}$ km. Who jogged a longer distance? How much longer?

6. There were $3\frac{1}{6}$ cakes on the table. After breakfast, there were $1\frac{2}{3}$ cakes left. How many cakes were eaten?

7. A container has a capacity of 3 liters. It contains $1\frac{3}{4}$ liters of water. How much more water is needed to fill the container?

8. Ann planned to spend $1\frac{1}{2}$ hours to cook a meal. She finished the cooking in $1\frac{1}{12}$ hours. How much earlier did she finish the cooking?

9. The total length of two ribbons is $2\frac{3}{4}$ m. If one ribbon is $1\frac{1}{3}$ m long, what is the length of the other ribbon?

4 Product of a Fraction and a Whole Number

Lihua bought 12 eggs. She used $\frac{2}{3}$ of them to bake a cake. How many eggs did she use?

Method 1:

Divide 12 eggs into 3 equal groups.

2 groups are shaded to show $\frac{2}{3}$.

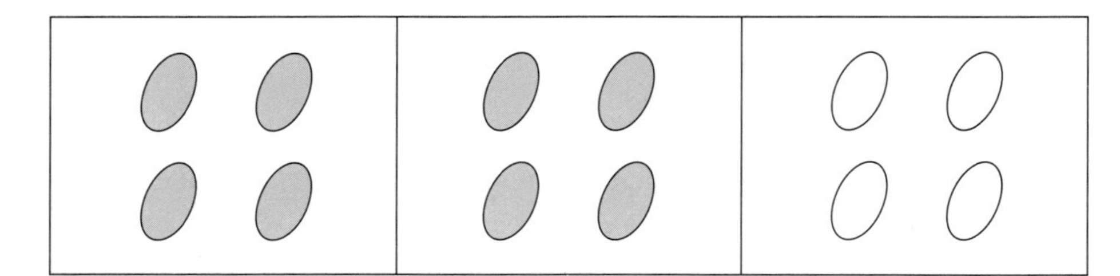

$\frac{2}{3}$ of 12 = ■

She used ■ eggs.

Method 2:

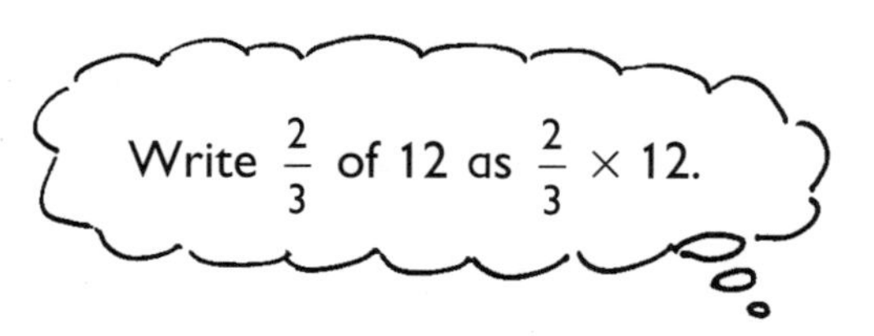

$$\frac{2}{3} \times 12 = \frac{2 \times 12}{3}$$

$$= ■$$

She used ■ eggs.

1. (a) Multiply $\frac{2}{3}$ by 5.

$$\frac{2}{3} \times 5 = \frac{2 \times 5}{3}$$
$$= \square$$

(b) Multiply 5 by $\frac{2}{3}$.

$$5 \times \frac{2}{3} = \frac{5 \times 2}{3}$$
$$= \square$$

2. Find the value of $\frac{3}{8} \times 20$.

Method 1:

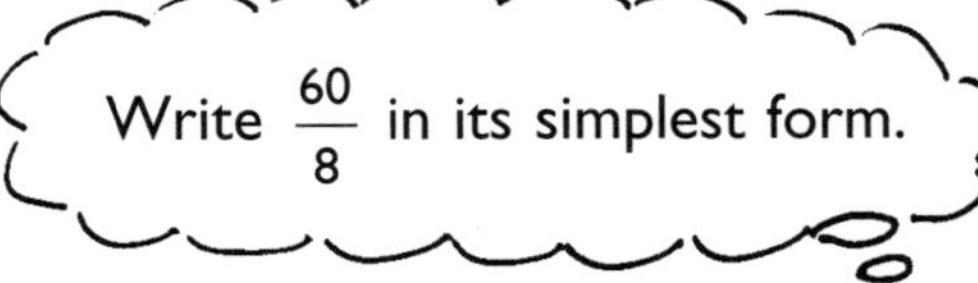

$$\frac{3}{8} \times 20 = \frac{3 \times 20}{8}$$
$$= \frac{60}{8}$$
$$= \square$$

Method 2:

$$\frac{3}{8} \times 20 = \frac{3 \times \cancel{20}^{5}}{\cancel{8}_{2}}$$
$$= \frac{3 \times 5}{2}$$
$$= \square$$

4 is a common factor of 20 and 8.
Divide 20 and 8 by 4.

Method 3:

$$\frac{3}{\cancel{8}_{2}} \times \cancel{20}^{5} = \frac{3 \times 5}{2}$$
$$= \square$$

3. How many months are there in $\frac{5}{6}$ of a year?

$\frac{5}{6}$ of a year $= \frac{5}{6} \times 12$ months

$=$ ■ months

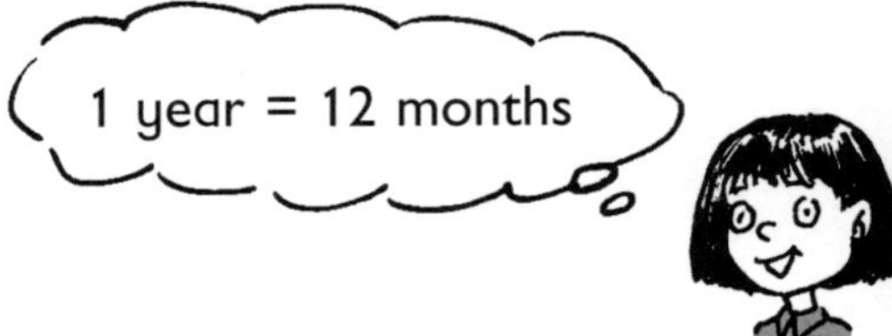

Conversion of Measurements

Length

1 m = 100 cm
1 km = 1000 m
1 yd = 3 ft
1 ft = 12 in.
1 mi = 5280 ft

Weight

1 kg = 1000 g
1 lb = 16 oz

Volume of liquid/capacity

1 ℓ = 1000 ml
1 gal = 4 qt
1 qt = 2 pt
1 qt = 4 c

Time

1 year = 12 months
1 week = 7 days
1 day = 24 hours
1 hour = 60 minutes
1 minute = 60 seconds

4. Find the missing number in each ■.

(a) $\frac{1}{2}$ min = ■ s
(b) $\frac{7}{10}$ kg = ■ g
(c) $\frac{2}{5}$ km = ■ m
(d) $\frac{3}{10}$ ℓ = ■ ml
(e) $\frac{3}{4}$ year = ■ months
(f) $\frac{1}{6}$ h = ■ min
(g) $\frac{2}{3}$ yd = ■ ft
(h) $\frac{1}{4}$ lb = ■ oz
(i) $\frac{3}{4}$ gal = ■ qt

5. Express $2\frac{3}{4}$ h in hours and minutes.

$\frac{3}{4}$ h $= \frac{3}{4} \times 60$ min = ■ min

$2\frac{3}{4}$ h = ■ h ■ min

6. Find the missing number in each ■.

(a) $2\frac{1}{3}$ h = ■ h ■ min
(b) $4\frac{2}{3}$ yd = ■ yd ■ ft
(c) $5\frac{1}{4}$ gal = ■ gal ■ qt
(d) $3\frac{1}{2}$ km = ■ km ■ m
(e) $14\frac{9}{10}$ ℓ = ■ ℓ ■ ml
(f) $6\frac{1}{4}$ years = ■ years ■ months

Workbook Exercise 19

7. Express $3\frac{2}{5}$ km in meters.

$3 \text{ km} = 3000 \text{ m}$

$\frac{2}{5} \text{ km} = \frac{2}{5} \times 1000 \text{ m}$

$= \blacksquare \text{ m}$

$3\frac{2}{5} \text{ km} = \blacksquare \text{ m}$

8. Express $2\frac{1}{4}$ days in hours.

$2 \text{ days} = \blacksquare \text{ h}$

$\frac{1}{4} \text{ day} = \blacksquare \text{ h}$

$2\frac{1}{4} \text{ days} = \blacksquare \text{ h}$

9. Find the missing number in each $\blacksquare$.

(a) $2\frac{1}{2}$ m = $\blacksquare$ cm (b) $1\frac{1}{2}$ lb = $\blacksquare$ oz (c) $3\frac{1}{2}$ gal = $\blacksquare$ qt

(d) $2\frac{3}{4}$ years = $\blacksquare$ months (e) $1\frac{3}{10}$ ℓ = $\blacksquare$ ml (f) $4\frac{1}{3}$ min = $\blacksquare$ s

(g) $2\frac{1}{10}$ km = $\blacksquare$ m (h) $3\frac{1}{3}$ h = $\blacksquare$ min (i) $5\frac{3}{4}$ ft = $\blacksquare$ in.

Workbook Exercise 20

10. (a) What fraction of \$2 is 80¢?

\$2 = 200¢

$\frac{80}{200} = \blacksquare$

(b) Express 600 ml as a fraction of 1 liter.
(c) Express 90 cm as a fraction of 3 m.
(d) Express 45 seconds as a fraction of 1 minute.
(e) Express 50 minutes as a fraction of 2 hours.

Workbook Exercise 21

PRACTICE 3D

Find the value of each of the following in its simplest form.

	(a)	(b)	(c)
1.	$\frac{1}{2} \times 14$	$\frac{1}{4} \times 26$	$\frac{2}{5} \times 40$
2.	$30 \times \frac{4}{5}$	$40 \times \frac{2}{3}$	$15 \times \frac{5}{9}$
3.	$\frac{7}{3} \times 21$	$\frac{13}{5} \times 20$	$40 \times \frac{9}{8}$

Find the missing number in each ▇.

	(a)	(b)
4.	$\frac{2}{3}$ h = ▇ min	$\frac{3}{5}$ kg = ▇ g
5.	$\frac{4}{5}$ m = ▇ cm	$\frac{9}{10}$ km = ▇ m
6.	$8\frac{3}{4}$ years = ▇ years ▇ months	$3\frac{3}{5}$ ℓ = ▇ ℓ ▇ ml
7.	$9\frac{1}{4}$ lb = ▇ lb ▇ oz	$5\frac{1}{3}$ h = ▇ h ▇ min
8.	$3\frac{1}{2}$ ft = ▇ in.	$4\frac{1}{4}$ gal = ▇ qt
9.	$2\frac{7}{10}$ km = ▇ m	$4\frac{2}{3}$ days = ▇ h

10. (a) What fraction of \$1 is 90¢?
    (b) What fraction of 2 ℓ is 750 ml?
    (c) What fraction of 3 lb is 12 oz?

11. (a) Express 9 months as a fraction of 1 year.
    (b) Express 50 minutes as a fraction of 2 hours.
    (c) Express 8 in. as a fraction of 2 ft.

12. In an examination, 40 out of 44 students passed. What fraction of the students passed the examination?

13. Holly earns \$350 a month. She saves \$70 each month. What fraction of her earnings does she save?

5 Product of Fractions

(a) Color $\frac{3}{4}$ of a rectangle.

Cut out $\frac{1}{2}$ of the colored parts.

What fraction of the rectangle is cut out?

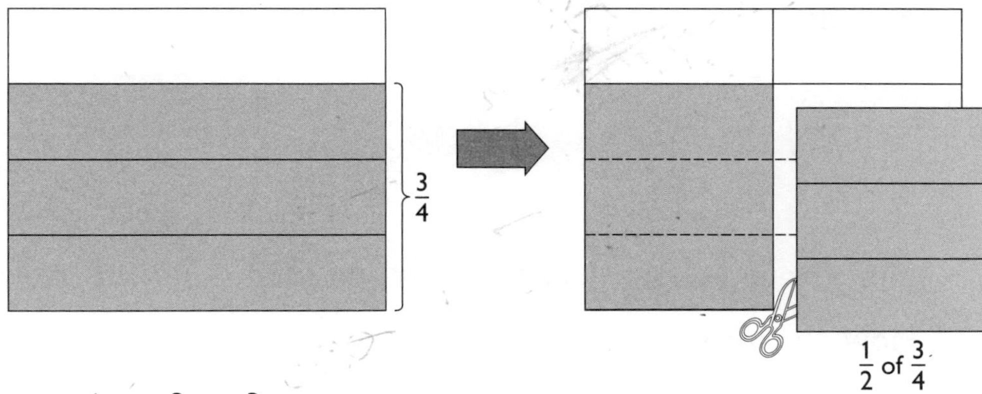

$\frac{1}{2}$ of $\frac{3}{4} = \frac{3}{8}$

$\frac{3}{8}$ of the rectangle is cut out.

$$\frac{1}{2} \times \frac{3}{4} = \frac{1 \times 3}{2 \times 4}$$
$$= \frac{3}{8}$$

Write $\frac{1}{2}$ of $\frac{3}{4}$ as $\frac{1}{2} \times \frac{3}{4}$.

(b) Color $\frac{1}{2}$ of a rectangle.

Write $\frac{3}{4}$ of $\frac{1}{2}$ as $\frac{3}{4} \times \frac{1}{2}$.

Cut out $\frac{3}{4}$ of the colored parts.

What fraction of the rectangle is cut out?

Is $\frac{1}{2}$ of $\frac{3}{4}$ the same as $\frac{3}{4}$ of $\frac{1}{2}$?

1. A flower garden occupies $\frac{1}{2}$ of a piece of land. $\frac{3}{5}$ of the garden is used for growing orchids. What fraction of the land is used for growing orchids?

$\frac{3}{5} \times \frac{1}{2} = $ ■

■ of the land is used for growing orchids.

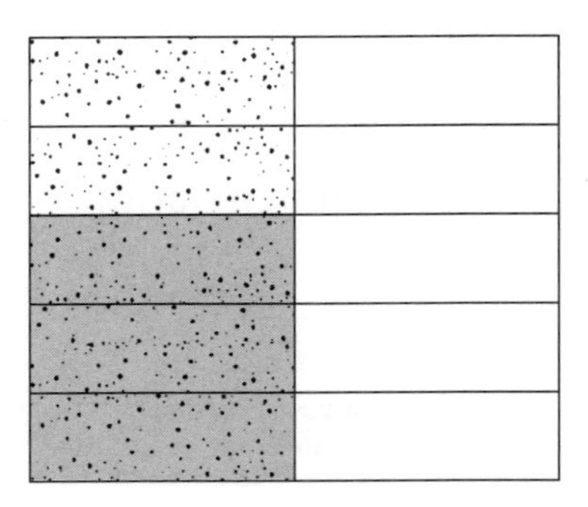

2. Mrs. Green bought $\frac{3}{5}$ lb of sugar. She used $\frac{3}{4}$ of it to make a cake. How much sugar did she use?

$\frac{3}{4} \times \frac{3}{5} = $ ■

She used ■ lb of sugar.

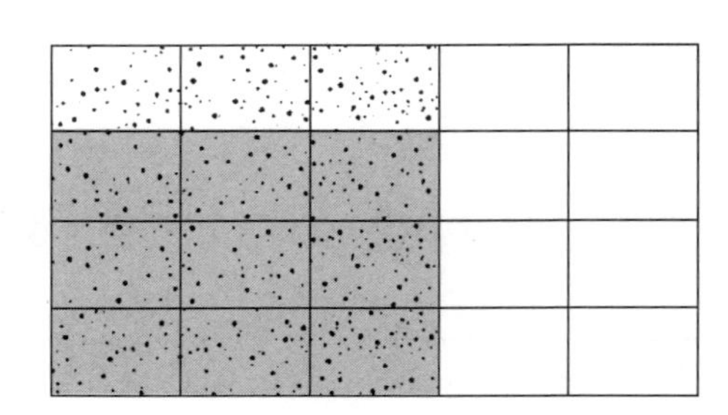

3. Find the area of a rectangle measuring $\frac{1}{3}$ m by $\frac{5}{6}$ m.

$\frac{1}{3} \times \frac{5}{6} = $ ■

The area of the rectangle is ■ m^2.

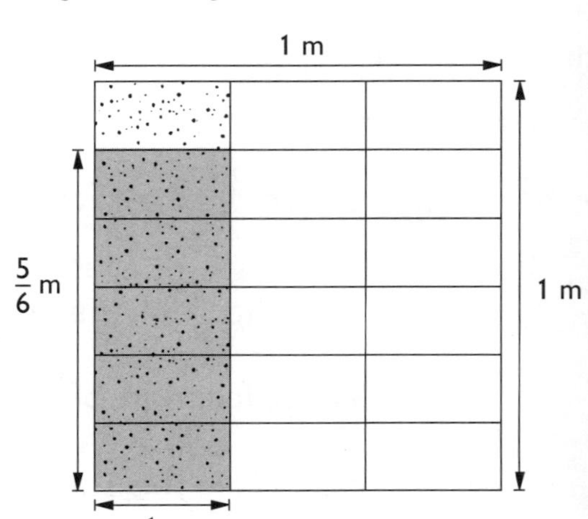

4. $\frac{2}{3}$ of a wall is painted red. $\frac{1}{4}$ of the remaining part is painted gray. What fraction of the wall is painted gray?

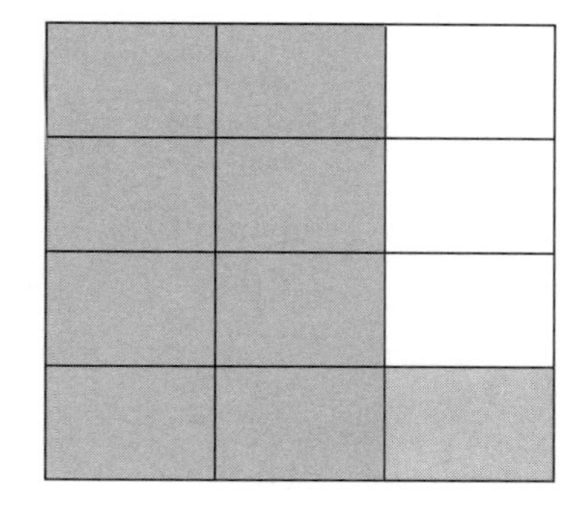

$1 - \frac{2}{3} = \frac{1}{3}$

The remaining part is $\frac{1}{3}$ of the wall.

$\frac{1}{4} \times \frac{1}{3} = \blacksquare$

$\blacksquare$ of the wall is painted gray.

5. Multiply $\frac{4}{5}$ by $\frac{2}{3}$.

$$\frac{4}{5} \times \frac{2}{3} = \frac{4 \times 2}{5 \times 3}$$
$$= \blacksquare$$

6. Find the product of $\frac{9}{10}$ and $\frac{5}{12}$.

Method 1:

$$\frac{9}{10} \times \frac{5}{12} = \frac{{}^{3}\cancel{9} \times \cancel{5}^{1}}{{}_{2}\cancel{10} \times \cancel{12}_{4}}$$
$$= \blacksquare$$

Method 2:

$$\frac{{}^{3}\cancel{9}}{{}_{2}\cancel{10}} \times \frac{\cancel{5}^{1}}{\cancel{12}_{4}} = \frac{3 \times 1}{2 \times 4}$$
$$= \blacksquare$$

7. Find the value of

(a) $\frac{1}{2}$ of $\frac{1}{2}$ (b) $\frac{1}{3}$ of $\frac{3}{4}$ (c) $\frac{1}{4}$ of $\frac{8}{9}$

(d) $\frac{5}{6} \times \frac{1}{5}$ (e) $\frac{3}{4} \times \frac{5}{6}$ (f) $\frac{4}{5} \times \frac{3}{8}$

(g) $\frac{5}{8} \times \frac{4}{9}$ (h) $\frac{1}{3} \times \frac{6}{7}$ (i) $\frac{5}{6} \times \frac{7}{10}$

(j) $\frac{15}{4} \times \frac{8}{3}$ (k) $\frac{9}{4} \times \frac{16}{3}$ (l) $\frac{12}{5} \times \frac{20}{9}$

Workbook Exercises 22 & 23

PRACTICE 3E

Find the value of each of the following in its simplest form.

	(a)	(b)	(c)
1.	$\frac{3}{8} \times \frac{1}{3}$	$\frac{4}{9} \times \frac{5}{8}$	$\frac{7}{8} \times \frac{3}{7}$
2.	$\frac{2}{7} \times \frac{7}{10}$	$\frac{8}{9} \times \frac{3}{4}$	$\frac{9}{10} \times \frac{5}{6}$
3.	$\frac{5}{6} \times \frac{2}{5}$	$\frac{3}{4} \times \frac{2}{3}$	$\frac{3}{10} \times \frac{5}{6}$
4.	$\frac{16}{3} \times \frac{9}{4}$	$\frac{14}{9} \times \frac{12}{7}$	$\frac{10}{7} \times \frac{14}{5}$
5.	$\frac{20}{7} \times \frac{7}{4}$	$\frac{11}{5} \times \frac{20}{11}$	$\frac{15}{8} \times \frac{8}{3}$

6. Shawn had a piece of string $\frac{1}{2}$ m long. He used $\frac{1}{3}$ of it to tie a box. Find the length of the string which was used to tie the box.

7. Kelley had $\frac{3}{4}$ qt of cooking oil. She used $\frac{2}{5}$ of it to fry some fish. How much oil did she use?

8. Mrs. Ruiz bought $\frac{4}{5}$ kg of beef. She cooked $\frac{3}{4}$ of it for lunch. How much beef did she cook?

9. Sally ate $\frac{1}{6}$ of a cake and gave $\frac{1}{5}$ of the remainder to her sister. What fraction of the cake did she give away?

10. Find the area of a rectangle which measures $\frac{5}{8}$ m by $\frac{3}{5}$ m.

6 Dividing a Fraction by a Whole Number

4 boys shared $\frac{2}{3}$ of a pie equally.

What fraction of the pie did each boy receive?

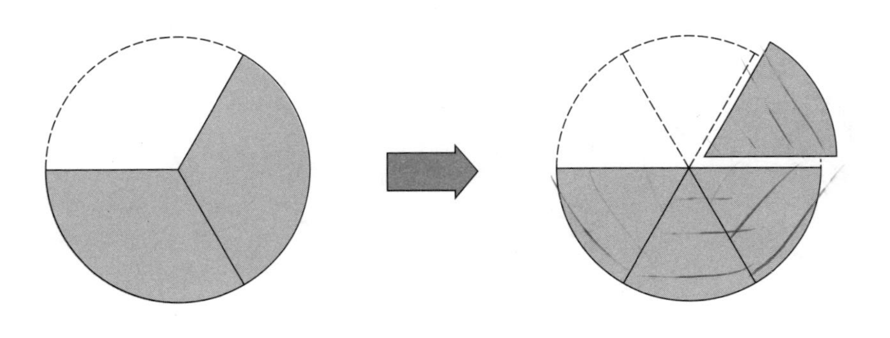

$$\frac{2}{3} \div 4 = \frac{1}{6}$$

Each boy received $\frac{1}{6}$ of the pie.

$$\frac{2}{3} \div 4 = \frac{1}{4} \text{ of } \frac{2}{3}$$

$$= \frac{1}{\cancel{4}_2} \times \frac{\cancel{2}^1}{3}$$

$$= \frac{1}{6}$$

Each boy received $\frac{1}{4}$ of $\frac{2}{3}$ of the pie.

Here is another way to divide $\frac{2}{3}$ by 4.

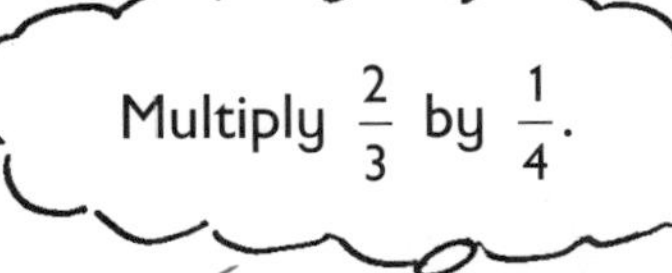

Multiply $\frac{2}{3}$ by $\frac{1}{4}$.

$$\frac{2}{3} \div 4 = \frac{^1\cancel{2}}{3} \times \frac{1}{\cancel{4}_2}$$

$$= \frac{1}{6}$$

1. Divide $\frac{2}{3}$ by 3.

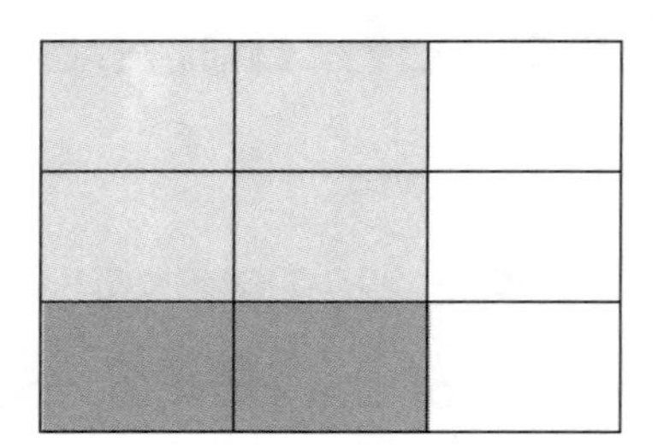

$$\frac{2}{3} \div 3 = \frac{2}{3} \times \frac{1}{3}$$

$$= \blacksquare$$

Dividing by 3 is the same as multiplying by $\frac{1}{3}$.

2. Divide.

(a) $\frac{3}{4} \div 6 = \frac{3}{4} \times \frac{1}{6} = \blacksquare$

(b) $\frac{3}{5} \div 9 = \frac{3}{5} \times \frac{1}{9} = \blacksquare$

(c) $\frac{5}{6} \div 5 = \frac{5}{6} \times \blacksquare = \blacksquare$

(d) $\frac{9}{10} \div 3 = \frac{9}{10} \times \blacksquare = \blacksquare$

3. Find the value of each of the following in its simplest form.

(a) $\frac{1}{3} \div 2$

(b) $\frac{4}{5} \div 3$

(c) $\frac{5}{7} \div 4$

(d) $\frac{4}{5} \div 4$

(e) $\frac{6}{7} \div 2$

(f) $\frac{2}{3} \div 8$

(g) $\frac{9}{16} \div 3$

(h) $\frac{3}{8} \div 6$

(i) $\frac{9}{10} \div 6$

Workbook Exercises 24 & 25

PRACTICE 3F

Find the value of each of the following in its simplest form.

	(a)	(b)	(c)
1.	$\frac{1}{3} \div 3$	$\frac{5}{6} \div 3$	$\frac{9}{10} \div 3$
2.	$\frac{3}{4} \div 5$	$\frac{1}{5} \div 4$	$\frac{8}{9} \div 6$
3.	$\frac{2}{5} \div 3$	$\frac{5}{9} \div 5$	$\frac{5}{6} \div 10$

4. A string of length $\frac{4}{5}$ m is cut into 2 equal pieces. What is the length of each piece?

5. $\frac{4}{5}$ of the money collected at a garage sale was divided equally among 4 clubs. What fraction of the money did each club receive?

6. 6 packets of cookies weigh $\frac{3}{10}$ kg. Find the weight of 1 packet of cookies.

7. Sara poured $\frac{2}{5}$ pt of fruit juice equally into 4 cups. How much fruit juice was there in each cup?

8. The perimeter of a square flower bed is $\frac{3}{4}$ m. Find the length of each side in meters.

9. Mrs. Jones divided $\frac{3}{4}$ kg of grapes equally among 6 children. How many kilograms of grapes did each child receive?

7 Word Problems

Melissa had \$125. She spent $\frac{2}{5}$ of the money and saved the rest. How much money did she save?

$$1 - \frac{2}{5} = \frac{3}{5}$$

First, I find what fraction of the money is saved.

She saved $\frac{3}{5}$ of the money.

$$\frac{3}{5} \times \$125 = \$\blacksquare$$

She saved \$■.

I do it in another way.

Amount of money spent $= \frac{2}{\cancel{5}_{1}} \times \$\cancel{125}^{25} = \$50$

Amount of money saved $= \$125 - \$50 = \$\blacksquare$

Here is yet another way. I find 1 unit first.

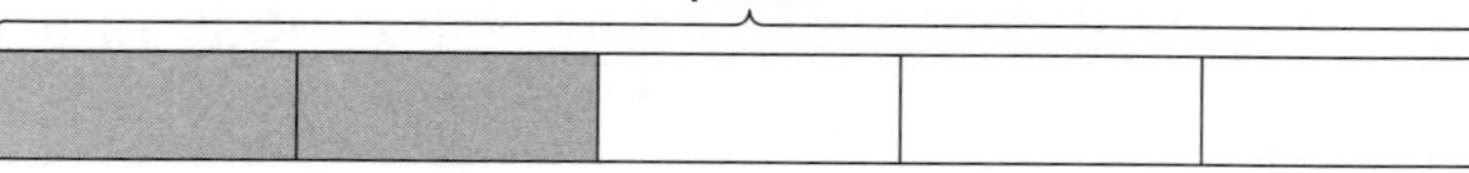

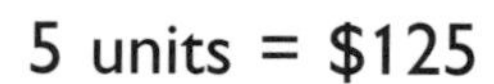

5 units = \$125

1 unit = \$■

Amount of money saved = 3 units = \$■

1. There are 96 children in a library. $\frac{5}{8}$ of them are girls. How many boys are there?

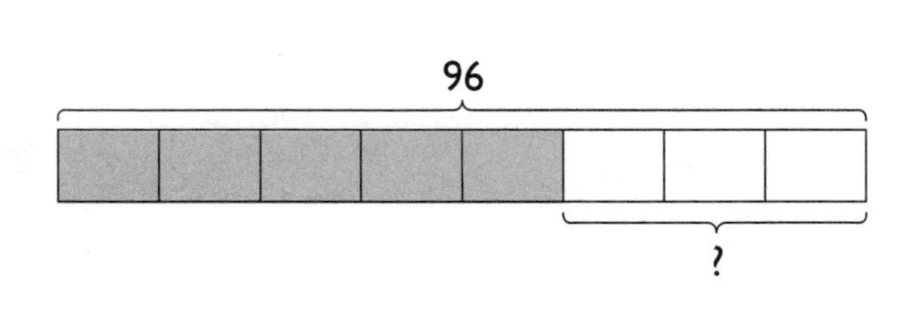

2. David had \$40. He spent $\frac{1}{5}$ of the money on a storybook and $\frac{3}{10}$ on a calculator. How much did he spend altogether?

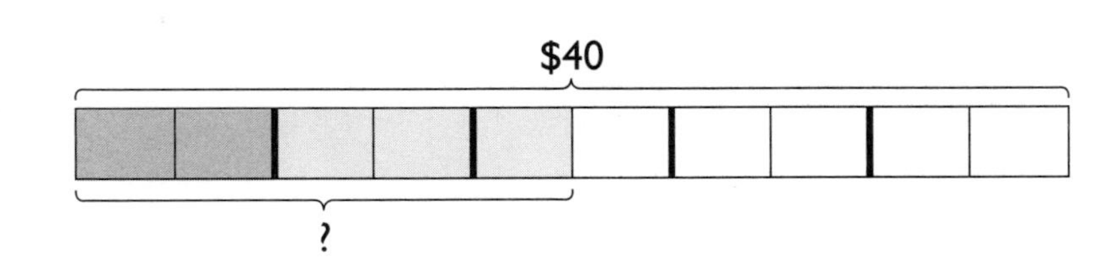

3. Scott had some eggs. He sold $\frac{5}{8}$ of them. If he sold 300 eggs, how many eggs did he have at first?

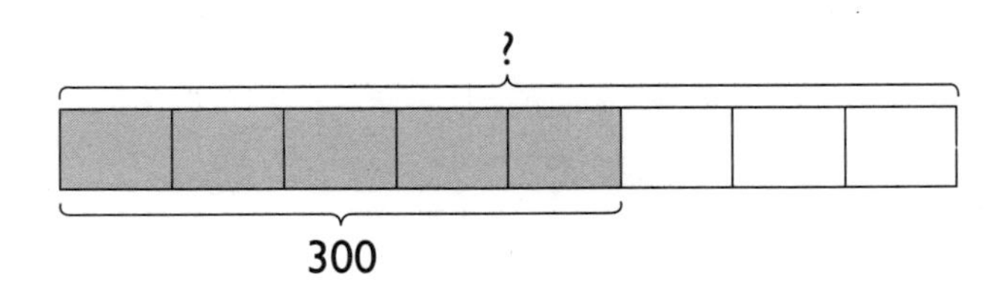

Workbook Exercises 26 & 27

4. Jim had 360 stamps. He sold $\frac{1}{3}$ of them on Monday and $\frac{1}{4}$ of the remainder on Tuesday. How many stamps did he sell on Tuesday?

Method 1:

First, I find what fraction of the stamps were left on Monday.

$$1 - \frac{1}{3} = \frac{2}{3}$$

He had $\frac{2}{3}$ of the stamps left on Monday.

$$\frac{2}{\cancel{3}_1} \times \cancel{360}^{120} = 2 \times 120 = 240$$

Next, I find the number of stamps left on Monday.

He had 240 stamps left on Monday.

$$\frac{1}{4} \times 240 = ■$$

He sold ■ stamps on Tuesday.

Method 2:

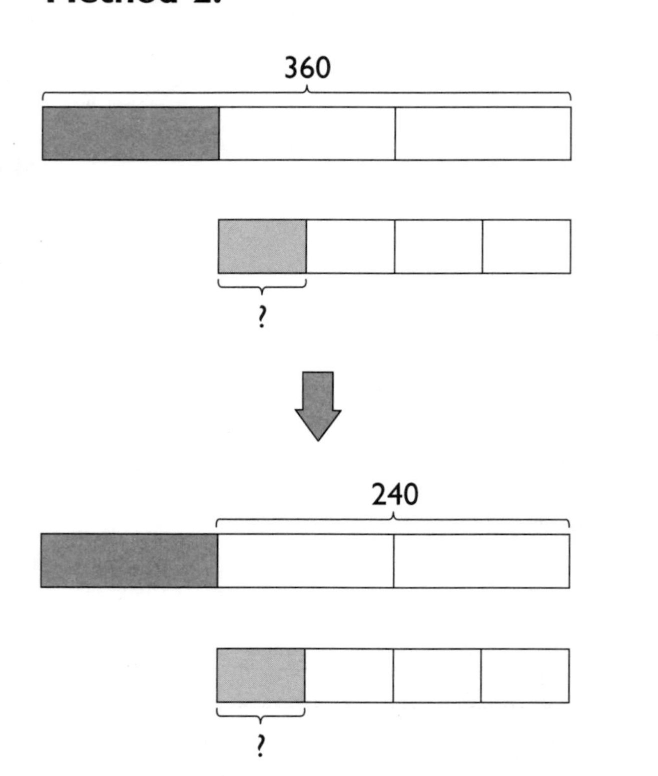

3 parts = 360
1 part = 120
2 parts = 240

Number of stamps left on Monday = 4 units = 240

Number of stamps sold on Tuesday = 1 unit = ■

5. Marisol made 300 tarts. She sold $\frac{3}{4}$ of them and gave $\frac{1}{3}$ of the remainder to her neighbor. How many tarts did she have left?

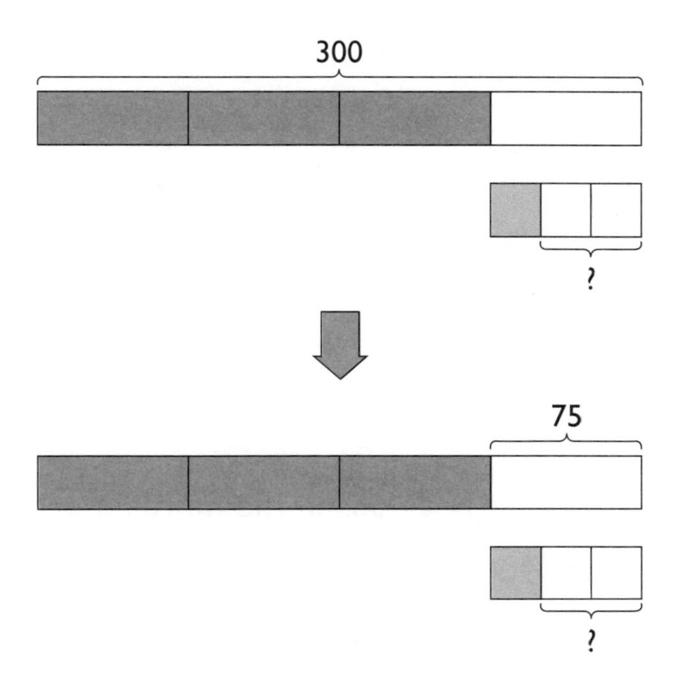

6. Mr. Anderson gave $\frac{2}{5}$ of his money to his wife and spent $\frac{1}{2}$ of the remainder. If he had $300 left, how much money did he have at first?

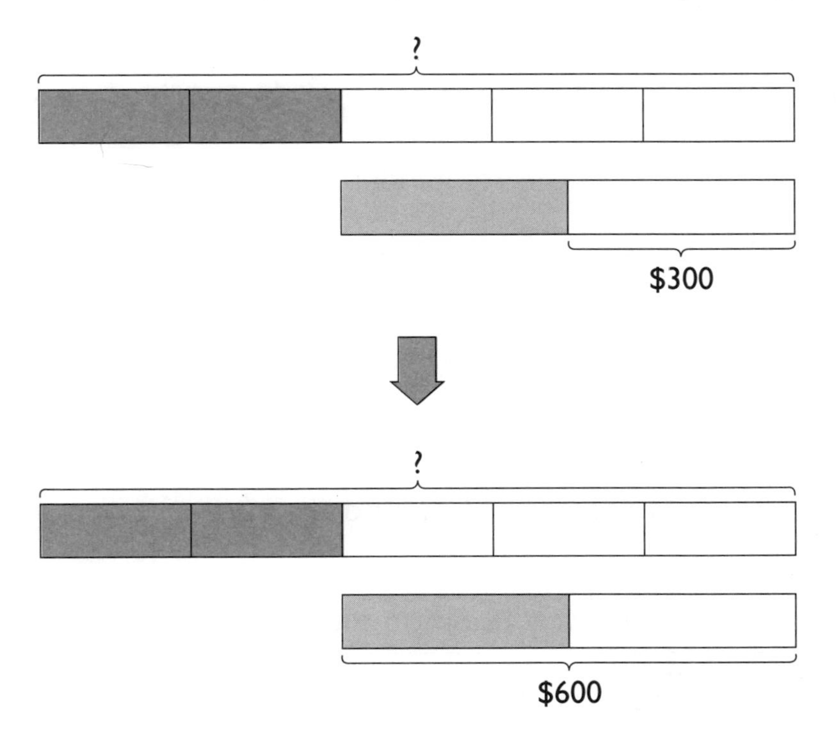

Workbook Exercises 28 & 29

PRACTICE 3G

1. $\frac{3}{7}$ of the apples in a box are red apples. The rest are green apples. There are 24 green apples. How many apples are there altogether?

2. After spending $\frac{2}{5}$ of his money on a toy car, Josh had $42 left. How much money did he have at first?

3. Mr. Ray had $400. He spent $\frac{2}{5}$ of it on a vacuum cleaner and $\frac{1}{4}$ of the remainder on a fan. How much money did he have left?

4. A vendor sold $\frac{2}{3}$ of his hot dogs in the morning and $\frac{1}{6}$ in the afternoon. He sold 200 hot dogs altogether. How many hot dogs did he have left?

5. Mrs. Gray bought some eggs. She used $\frac{1}{2}$ of them to make tarts and $\frac{1}{4}$ of the remainder to make a cake. She had 9 eggs left. How many eggs did she buy?

6. Tyrone bought a bag of marbles. $\frac{1}{4}$ of the marbles were blue, $\frac{1}{8}$ were green and $\frac{1}{5}$ of the remainder were yellow. If there were 24 yellow marbles, how many marbles did he buy?

7. Jeff gave $\frac{1}{4}$ of a sum of money to his wife. Then he divided the remainder equally among his 4 children.
   (a) What fraction of the sum of money did each child receive?
   (b) If each child received $600, find the sum of money.

8. Rosa read 10 pages of a book on Monday. She read $\frac{1}{3}$ of the remainder on Tuesday. If she still had 24 pages to read, how many pages were there in the book?

REVIEW A

1. Write the following in figures.
   (a) Five hundred fifteen thousand, four hundred seven
   (b) Four million, six hundred thousand

2. Write the following in words.
   (a) 872,520 (b) 1,034,000 (c) 4,500,000 (d) 162,003

3. What is the value of the digit 9 in 9,364,000?

4. Which one of the following numbers has the digit 6 in the ten thousands place?
   6,541,000, 640,059, 546,109, 5,164,000

5. (a) Round off $437,549 to the nearest $1000.
   (b) Round off 42,652 km to the nearest 1000 km.

6. The population of Marina Town is 280,524. Round off the number to the nearest 1000.

7. A house is sold for about $2,400,000. Which one of the following could be the actual selling price of the house?
   $2,356,000 $2,299,000 $2,460,000 $2,310,000

8. (a) Write down a common factor of 24 and 32.
   (b) Write down a common multiple of 8 and 10.

9. Round each number to the nearest 1000.
   Then estimate the value of
   (a) 3472 + 1607 (b) 29,074 + 5872
   (c) 9035 – 5712 (d) 14,236 – 6223

10. What is the missing number in each ■?
    3600, ■, 4800, 5400, ■

11. Estimate the value of
    (a) 3268×7 (b) 4825×63
    (c) $4312 \div 6$ (d) $7134 \div 82$

12. Multiply or divide.
    (a) 2650×600 (b) 1245×4000 (c) $34,400 \times 80$
    (d) $1280 \div 80$ (e) $1290 \div 80$ (f) $84,000 \div 7000$

13. Multiply or divide.

(a) 36×28 (b) 52×75 (c) 615×32
(d) $994 \div 71$ (e) $864 \div 36$ (f) $301 \div 24$

14. Find the value of each of the following:

(a) $2 \times (28 + 36) - 49$
(b) $78 + 21 \div 3 - (6 + 25)$
(c) $50 - (225 \div 15 + 13)$
(d) $29 + (300 \div 10 - 3 \times 9)$
(e) $28 + 19 - 24$
(f) $12 - 9 \times 5 \div 15$
(g) $(42 + 14) \div 7 \times 5$
(h) $(59 + 13) \div (4 \times 2)$

15. Write each fraction in its simplest form.

(a) $\frac{6}{8}$ (b) $\frac{9}{15}$ (c) $\frac{16}{24}$ (d) $\frac{32}{40}$

16. Express each of the following as an improper fraction.

(a) $5\frac{3}{8}$ (b) $3\frac{7}{11}$ (c) $4\frac{5}{9}$ (d) $2\frac{3}{4}$

17. Express each of the following as a whole number or a mixed number in its simplest form.

(a) $\frac{20}{6}$ (b) $\frac{18}{4}$ (c) $\frac{33}{3}$ (d) $\frac{30}{8}$

18. Name two equivalent fractions for each of these fractions.

(a) $\frac{3}{4}$ (b) $\frac{2}{6}$ (c) $\frac{5}{9}$ (d) $\frac{11}{14}$

19. Divide. Express each answer as a fraction in its simplest form.

(a) $8 \div 12$ (b) $15 \div 54$ (c) $63 \div 18$ (d) $100 \div 35$

20. Which is greater?

(a) $\frac{3}{2}$ or $\frac{5}{4}$ (b) $2\frac{1}{2}$ or $2\frac{1}{7}$ (c) $3\frac{8}{9}$ or 4
(d) $1\frac{6}{7}$ or $\frac{12}{7}$ (e) $4\frac{2}{3}$ or $\frac{9}{2}$ (f) $3\frac{1}{6}$ or $\frac{16}{5}$

21. Arrange the fractions in order, beginning with the smallest.

(a) $1\frac{3}{4}$, $\frac{9}{4}$, $1\frac{5}{8}$, $\frac{9}{2}$
(b) $1\frac{2}{8}$, $\frac{36}{5}$, $1\frac{2}{3}$, $\frac{8}{2}$

22. What number must be added to $4\frac{2}{9}$ to make 5?

23. How many quarters are there in $3\frac{1}{4}$?

24. Add or subtract. Give each answer in its simplest form.

(a) $\frac{5}{6} + \frac{3}{4}$ (b) $3\frac{3}{8} + \frac{5}{12}$ (c) $2\frac{1}{2} + 5\frac{4}{5}$

(d) $6 - \frac{6}{7}$ (e) $4\frac{3}{4} - \frac{2}{3}$ (f) $6\frac{1}{3} - 2\frac{3}{5}$

25. Multiply or divide.

(a) $\frac{7}{20} \times 4$ (b) $24 \times \frac{5}{8}$ (c) $35 \times \frac{2}{5}$

(d) $\frac{3}{4} \times \frac{8}{9}$ (e) $\frac{5}{8} \times \frac{14}{15}$ (f) $\frac{8}{12} \times \frac{16}{20}$

(g) $\frac{3}{5} \div 3$ (h) $\frac{7}{8} \div 2$ (i) $\frac{4}{7} \div 12$

26. (a) Express $\frac{3}{5}$ m in centimeters.

(b) Express $1\frac{7}{10}$ kg in kilograms and grams.

(c) Express $2\frac{3}{4}$ lb in pounds and ounces.

27. (a) Express 4 months as a fraction of 1 year.

(b) Express 48 minutes as a fraction of $1\frac{1}{2}$ hours.

(c) Express 1 pt as a fraction of $3\frac{1}{2}$ qt.

28. Ashley had 600 cookies. She packed them into packets of 24. How many packets of cookies did she get?

29. There are 2204 children in a school. 925 of them are girls. How many more boys than girls are there?

30. 3 pieces of ribbon, each 85 cm long, are cut from a length of ribbon 3 m long. What is the length of the remaining piece of ribbon?

31. Peter, John and Dan shared $1458 equally. Peter used part of his share to buy a bicycle and had $139 left. What was the cost of the bicycle?

32. Oranges are packed in a box in 4 layers. Each layer has 6 rows of oranges with 8 oranges in each row. How many oranges are there in the box?

33. Mrs. McCall has 1400 tarts. If she sells all of them at 80 cents each, how much money will she receive?

34. Haley answered 28 out of 32 problems correctly. What fraction of the problems did she answer correctly?

35. Bonita bought $2\frac{1}{5}$ kg of potatoes and $1\frac{1}{2}$ kg of carrots. How much more potatoes than carrots did she buy?

36. There are 42 students in Miss Brown's class. $\frac{3}{7}$ of them wear glasses. How many students wear glasses?

37. Danny bought 6 packets of drink. Each packet contained $\frac{1}{4}$ liter of drink. Find the total amount of drink in liters.

38. Mrs. Meier had $\frac{3}{5}$ kg of sugar. She used $\frac{1}{4}$ of it to make cookies. How much sugar did she use to make the cookies?

39. Mrs. Law bought $\frac{1}{2}$ of a cake. She cut it into 4 equal pieces. What fraction of the whole cake is each piece?

40. Mr. Ricci spent $\frac{1}{3}$ of his salary on food and $\frac{2}{5}$ of the remainder on transport.
    (a) What fraction of his salary did he have left?
    (b) If he had $600 left, find his salary.

41. Nicole bought 6 m of cloth to make a skirt and 3 shirts. She used $1\frac{3}{4}$ m for the skirt and $\frac{3}{4}$ m for each shirt. How much cloth did she have left?

42. David had 1280 eggs. He sold $\frac{3}{5}$ of them on Saturday and $\frac{1}{4}$ of the remainder on Sunday. Find the total number of eggs sold on the two days.

4 Area of Triangle

1 Finding the Area of a Triangle

Find the area of each shaded triangle and its related rectangle.

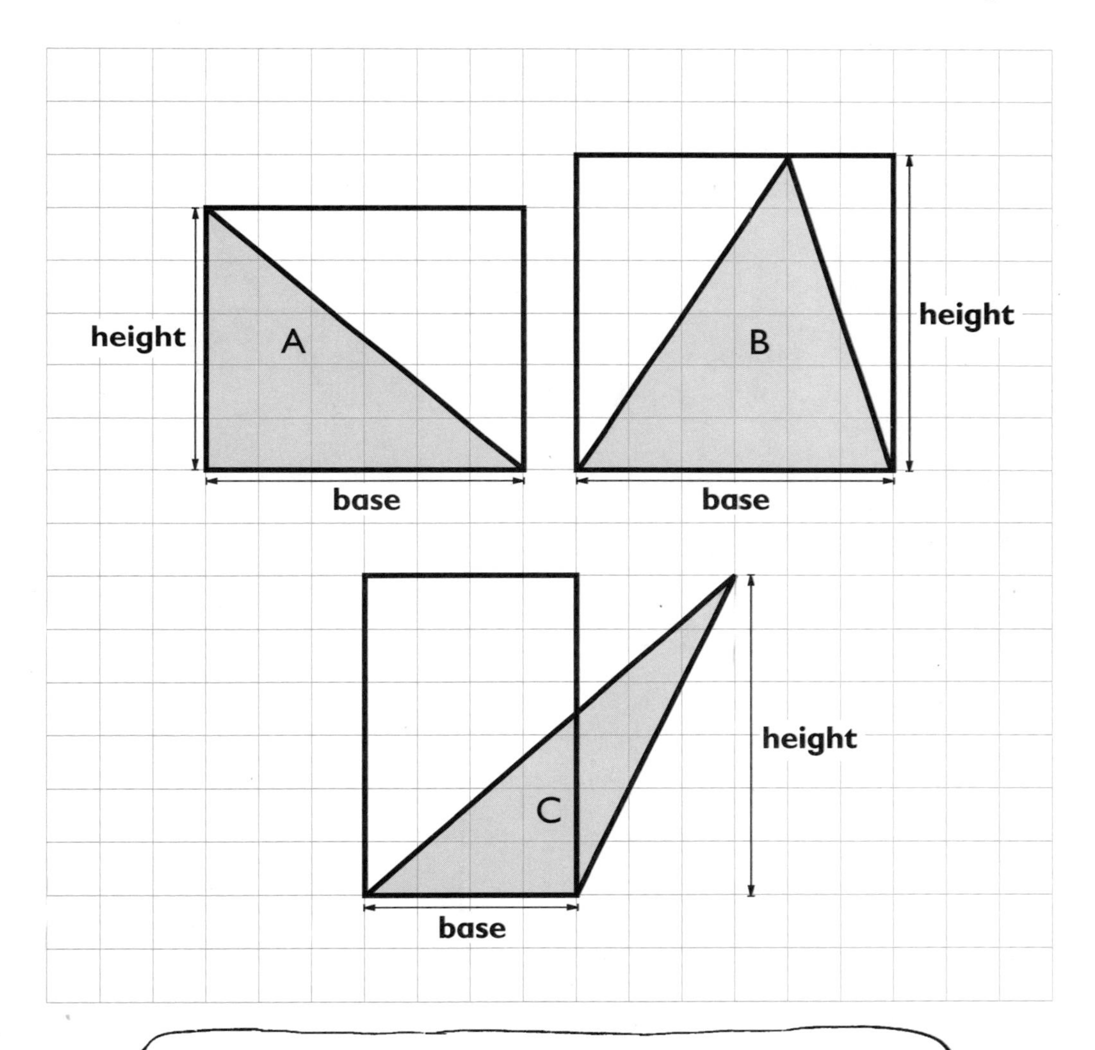

Compare the area of each triangle with the area of its related rectangle.

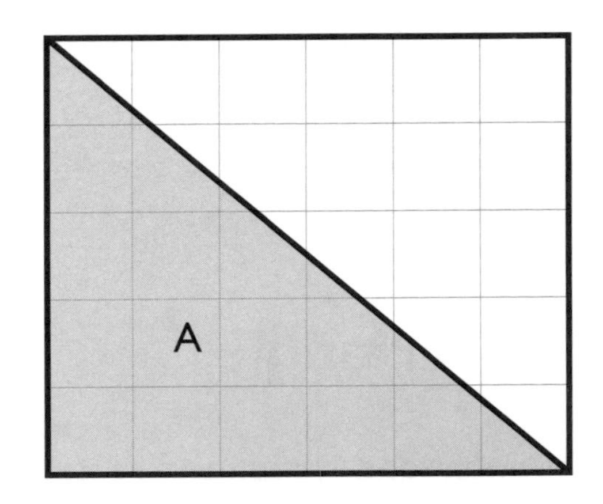

Area of related rectangle
= 6 × 5 = 30 square units

Area of triangle A
= ▇ square units

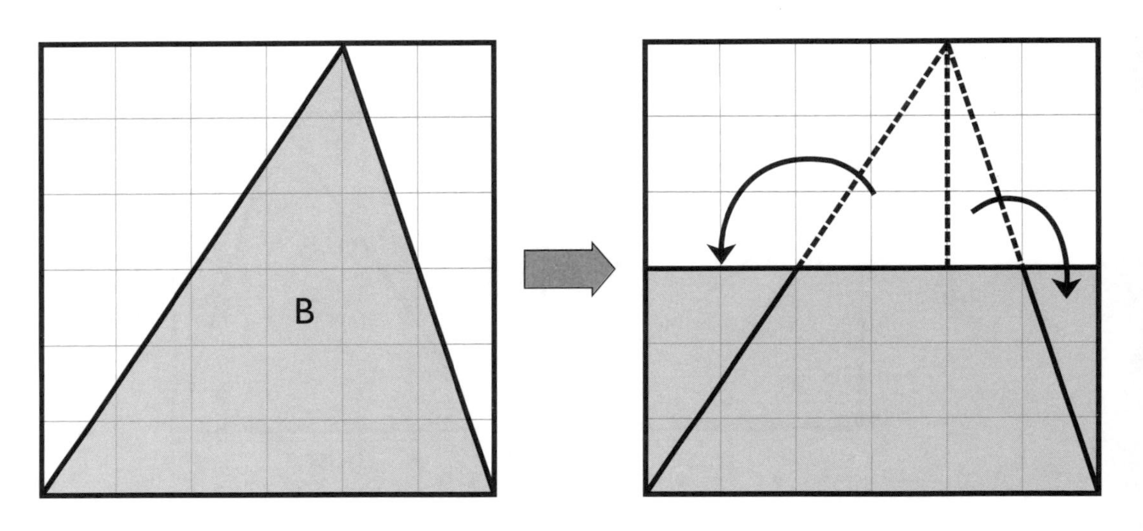

Area of related rectangle = 6 × 6 = 36 square units
Area of triangle B = ▇ square units

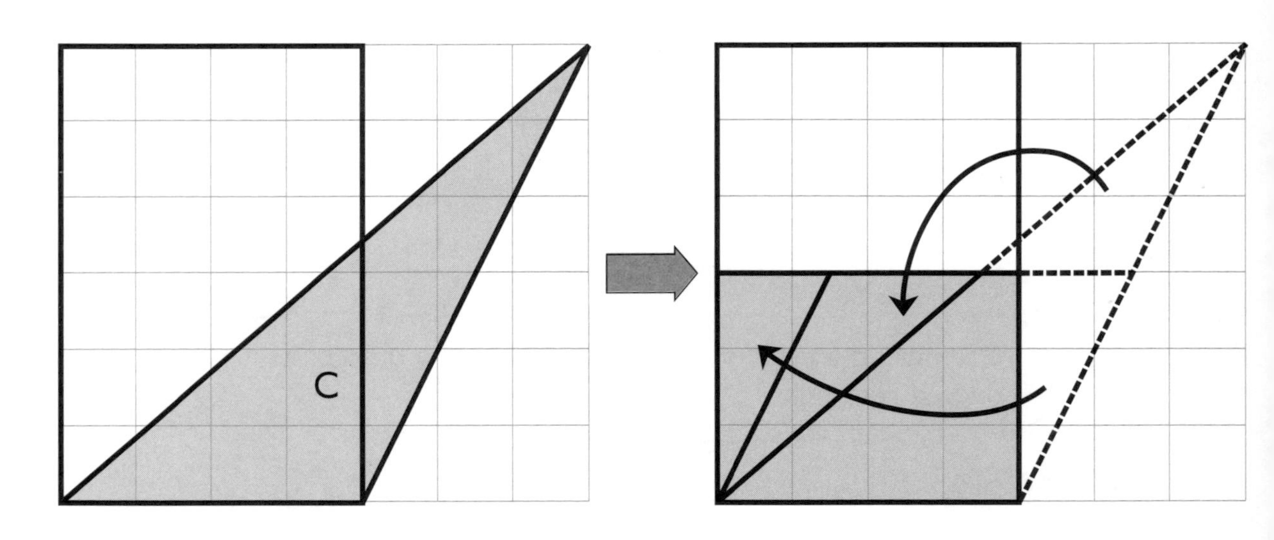

Area of related rectangle = 4 × 6 = 24 square units
Area of triangle C = ▇ square units

Area of triangle = $\frac{1}{2}$ × Area of related rectangle

Area of triangle = $\frac{1}{2}$ × Base × Height

1. Find the area of each triangle.

(a)

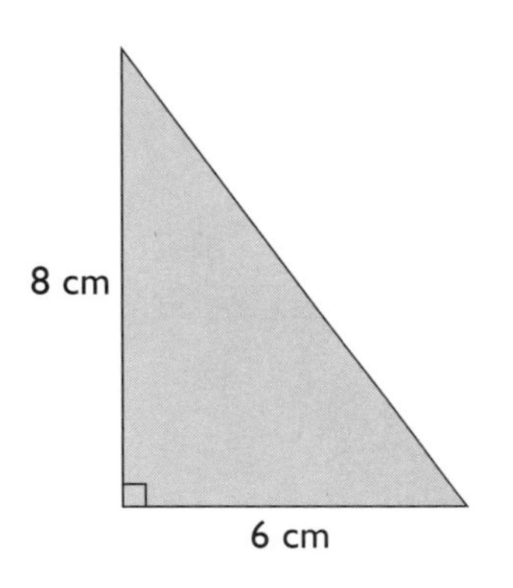

Area of the triangle

$= \frac{1}{2} \times 6 \times 8$

$= \blacksquare$ cm^2

(b)

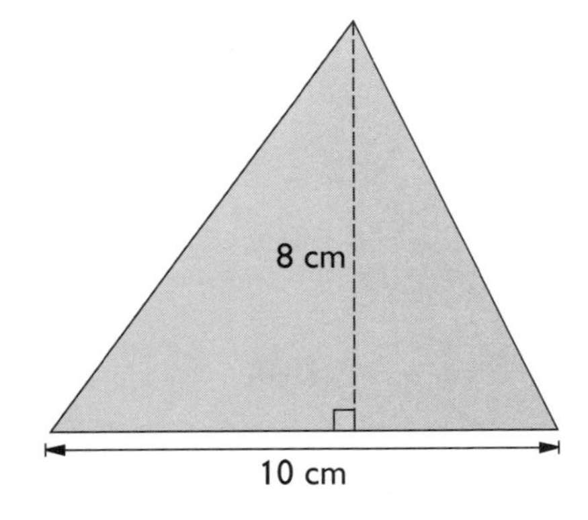

Area of the triangle

$= \frac{1}{2} \times 10 \times 8$

$= \blacksquare$ cm^2

(c)

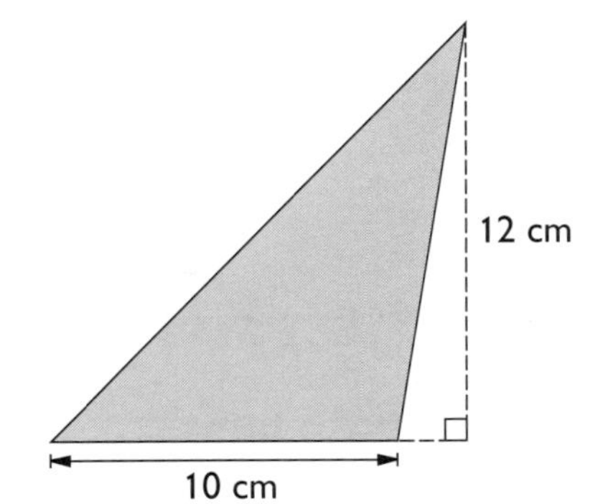

Area of the triangle

$= \frac{1}{2} \times 10 \times 12$

$= \blacksquare$ cm^2

2. Find the area of each shaded triangle.

(a)

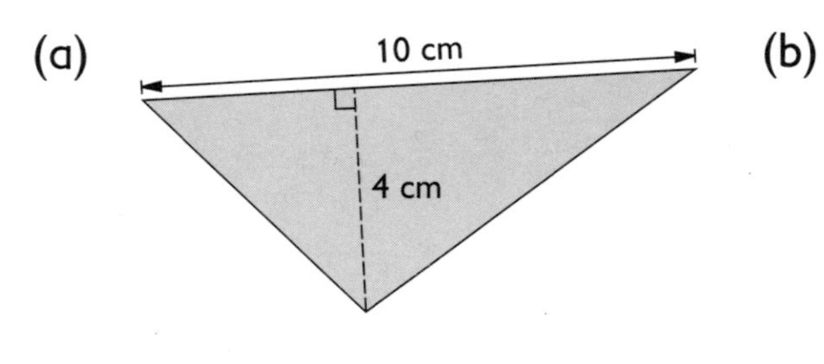

(b)

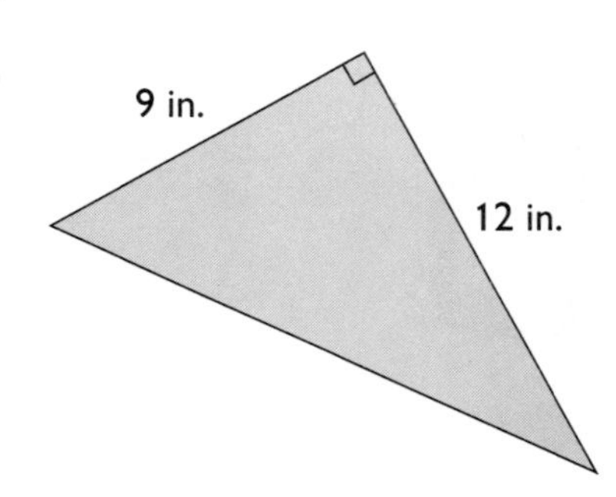

(c)

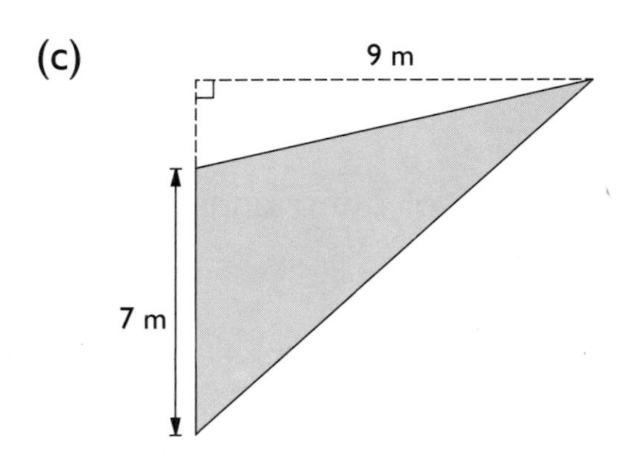

(d)

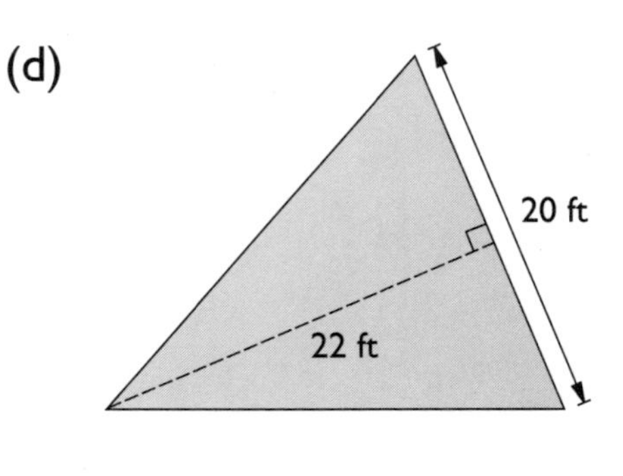

Workbook Exercises 30 to 32

3. Find the area of each shaded triangle.

(a)

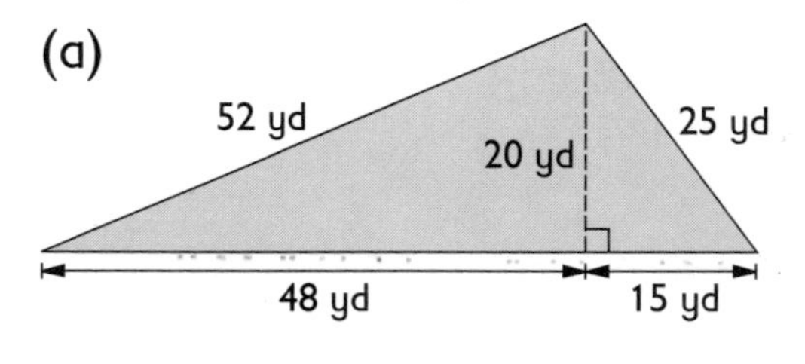

(b)

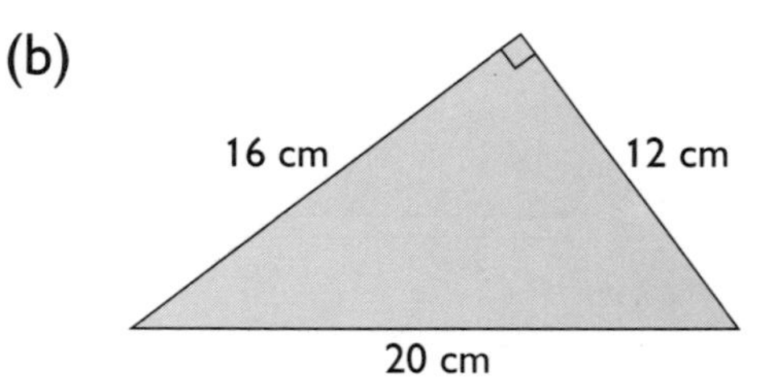

(c)

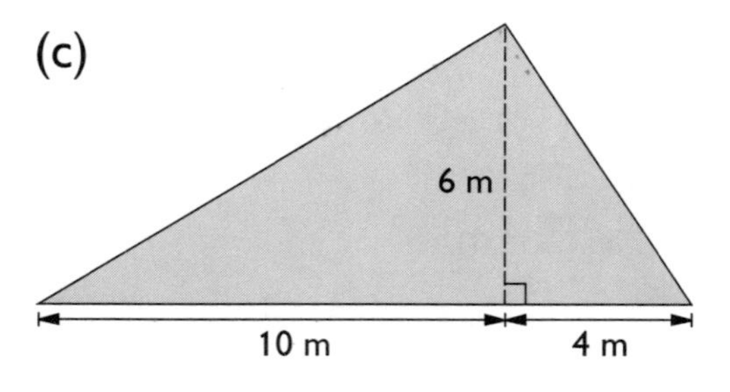

(d)

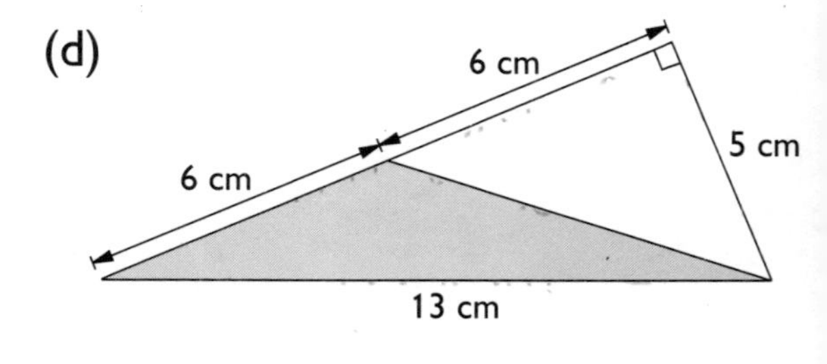

4. Find the shaded area of each rectangle.

(a)

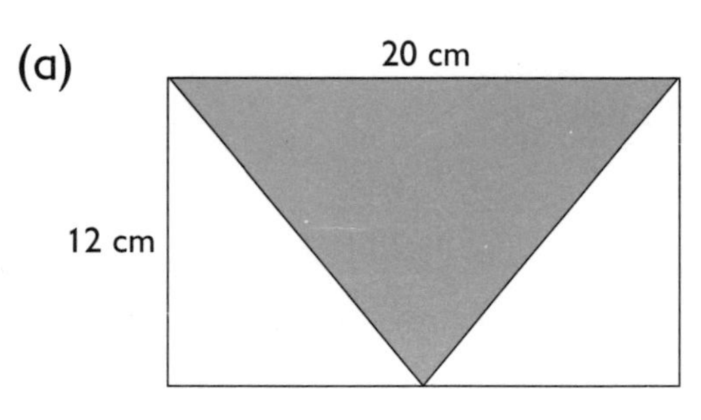

(b)

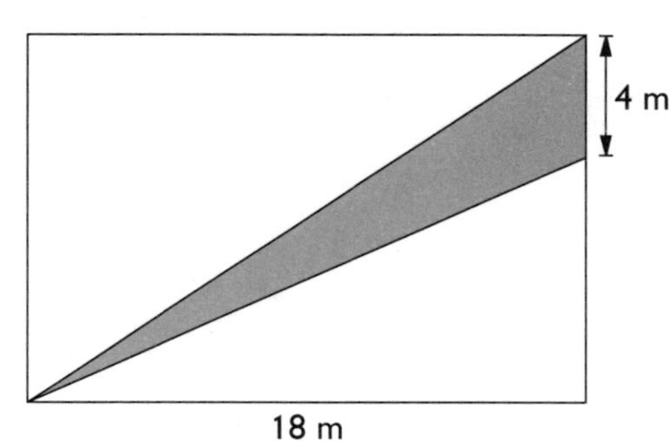

5. Find the shaded area of each rectangle.

(a)

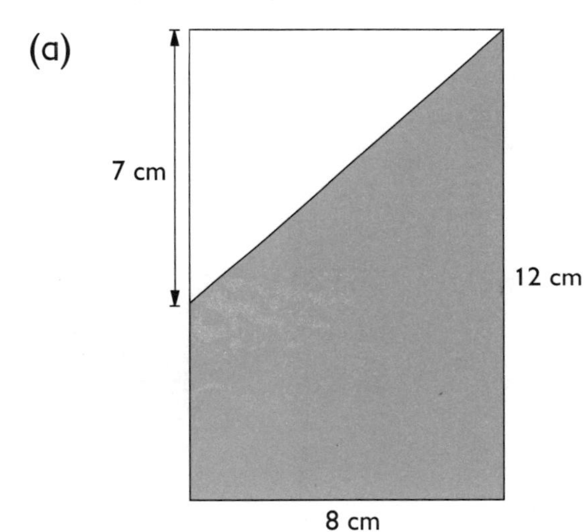

In each figure, the unshaded part is a triangle.

Find the area of the triangle first.

(b)

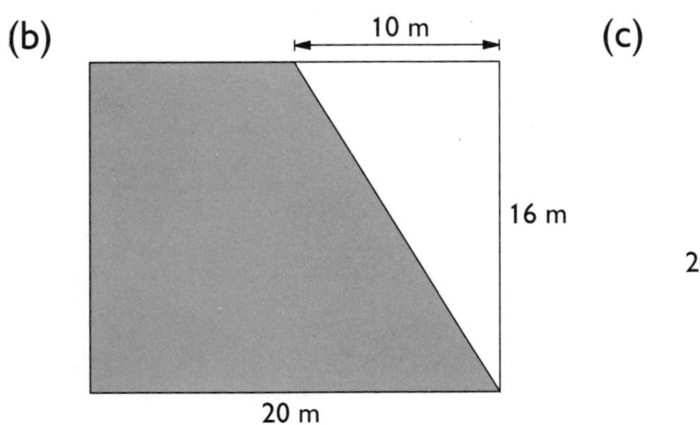

(c)

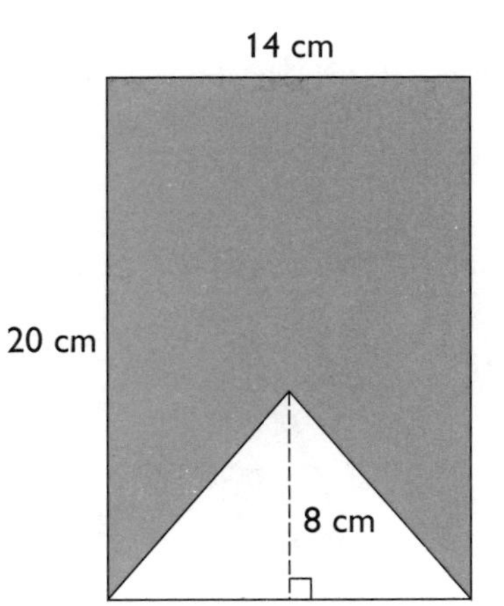

Workbook Exercise 33

PRACTICE 4A

1. Find the area of each shaded triangle.

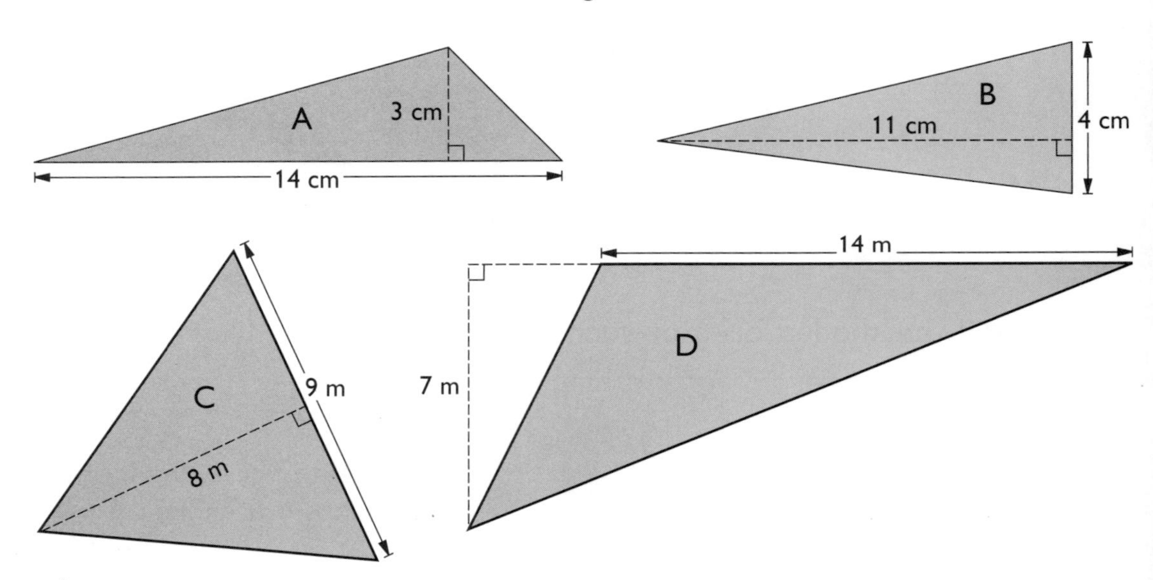

2. The perimeter of the shaded triangle is 60 cm. Find its area.

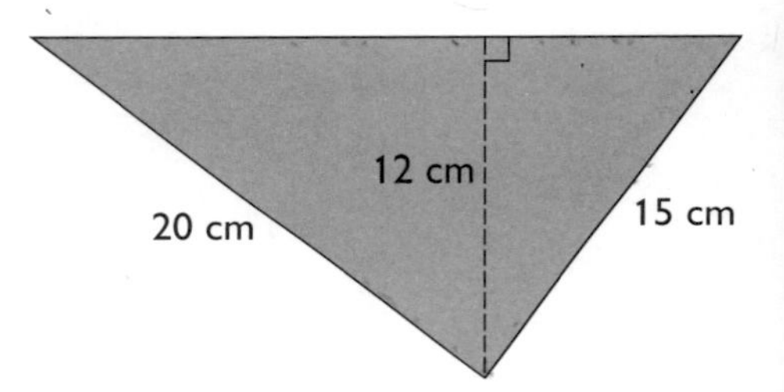

3. This figure is made up of 8 triangles. The base of each triangle is 6 cm and the height is 6 cm. What is the area of the figure?

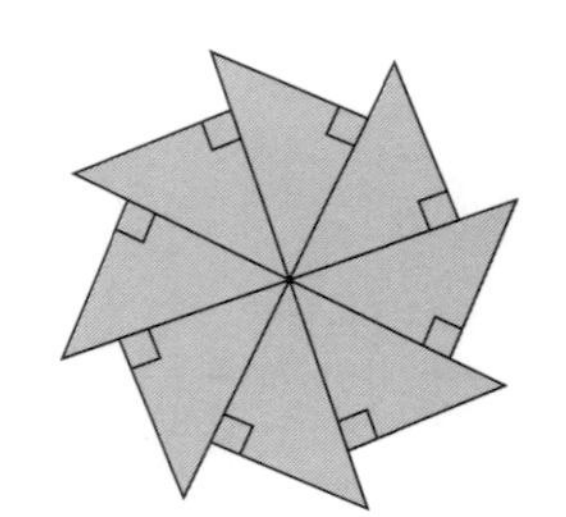

4. Find the area of each shaded figure.

(a)

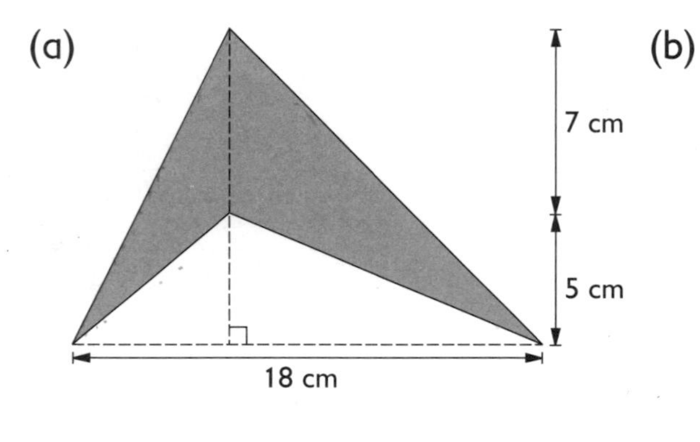

(b)

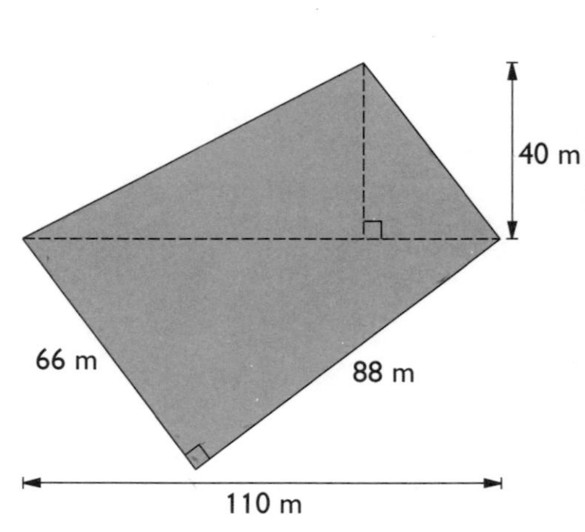

5 Ratio

1 Finding Ratio

David and John visited an art supply store. David bought 3 bottles of blue ink and 2 bottles of red ink.

The **ratio** of the number of bottles of blue ink to the number of bottles of red ink is 3 : 2.

John bought 5 boxes of blue pens and 2 boxes of red pens.

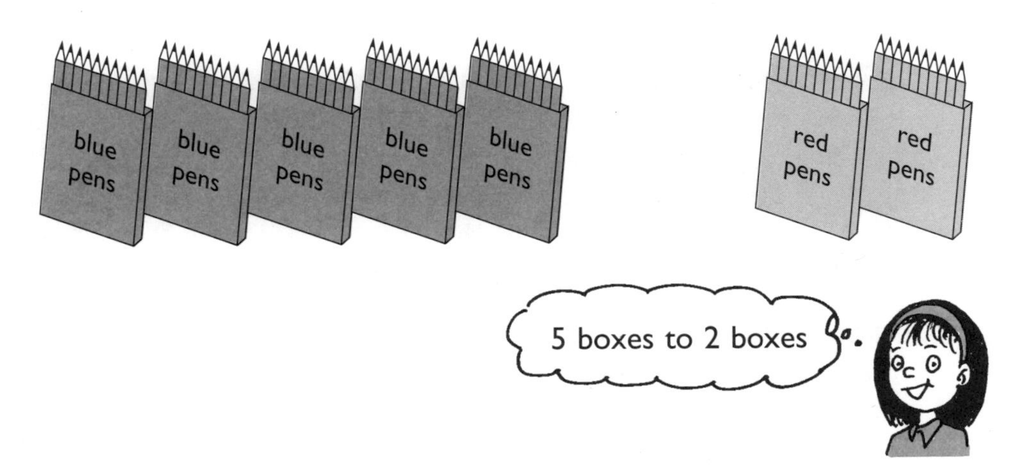

The **ratio** of the number of blue pens to the number of red pens is 5 : 2.

1. Ricardo mixed 3 cans of red paint with 1 can of white paint.

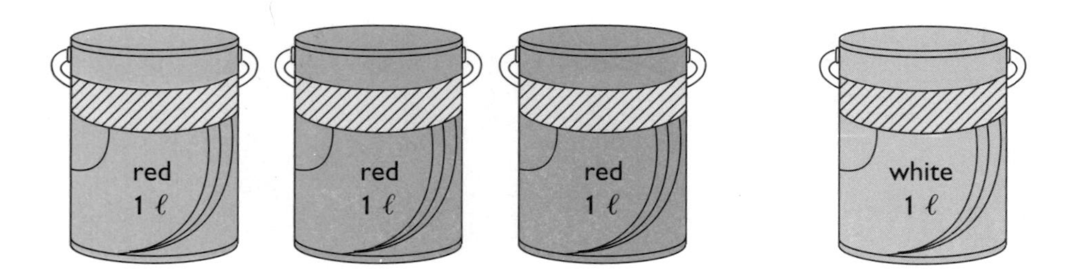

The ratio of the amount of red paint to the amount of white paint is 3 : 1.

The ratio of the amount of white paint to the amount of red paint is ■ : ■.

2.

The ratio of the number of jars of jam to the number of jars of jelly is 3 : 2.

The ratio of the number of jars of jelly to the number of jars of jam is ■ : ■.

3.

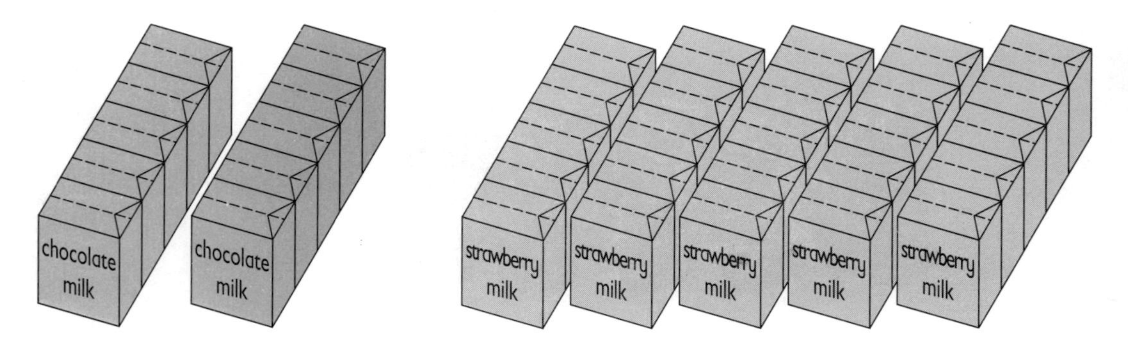

The ratio of the number of packets of chocolate milk to the number of packets of strawberry milk is ■ : ■.

The ratio of the number of packets of strawberry milk to the number of packets of chocolate milk is ■ : ■.

4. 1 unit

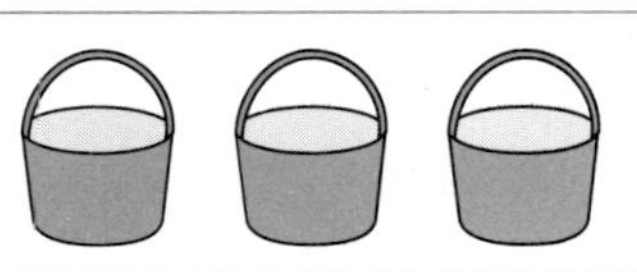 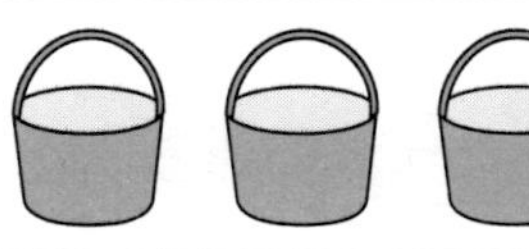 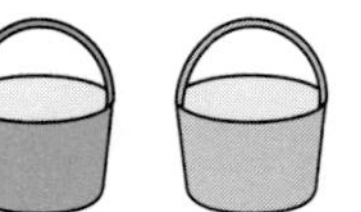  

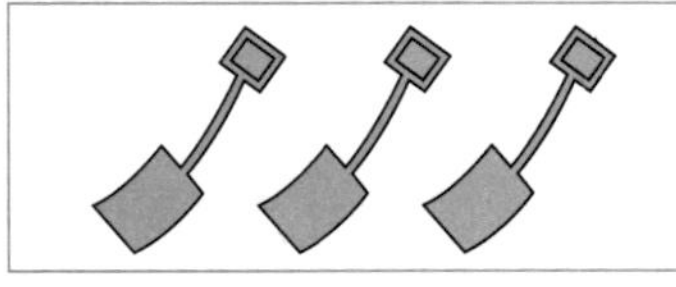 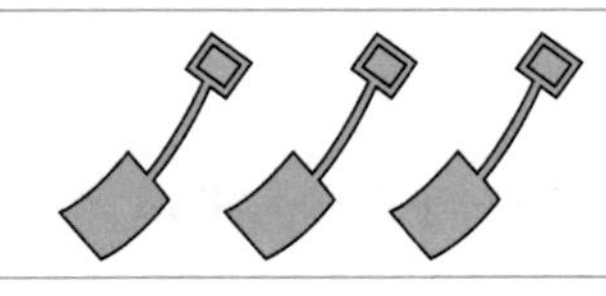

3 units to 2 units

The ratio of the number of buckets to the number of shovels is ■ : ■.

5.

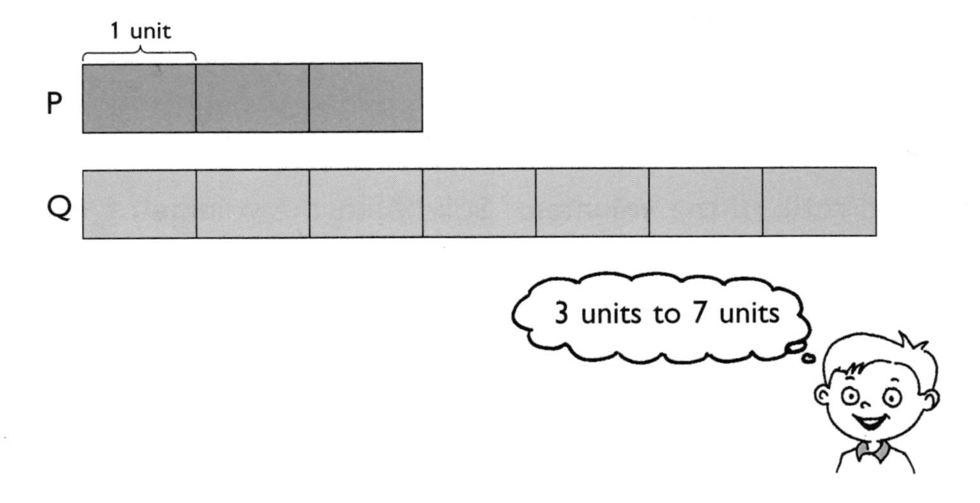

The ratio of the length of P to the length of Q is ■ : ■.

6.

The ratio of the length of the rectangle to its width is ■ : ■.

7.

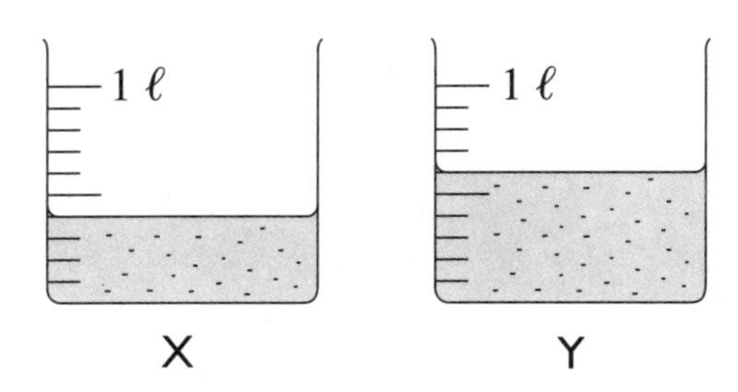

The ratio of the volume of sand in Container X to the volume of sand in Container Y is ■ : ■.

8.

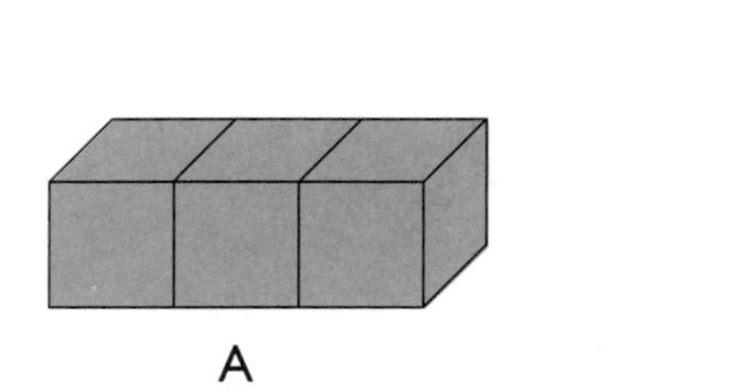

The ratio of the volume of Solid A to the volume of Solid B is ■ : ■.

9.

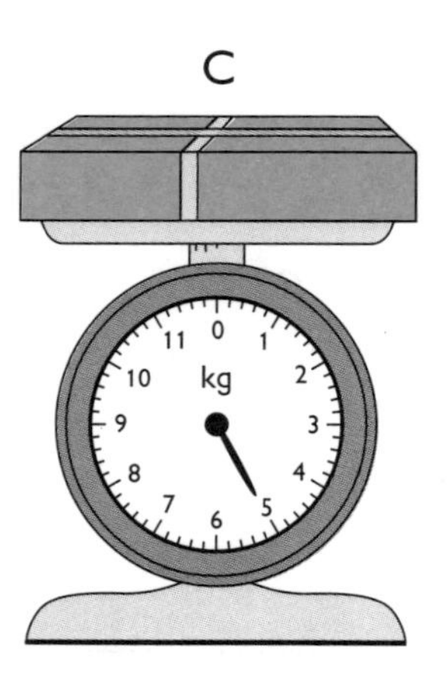

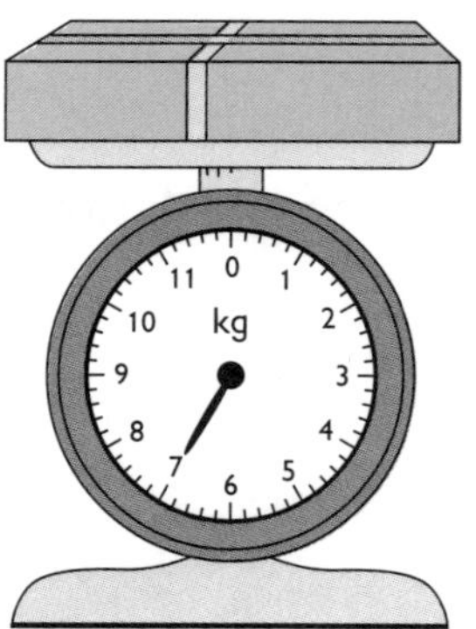

The ratio of the weight of Package C to the weight of Package D is ■ : ■.

Workbook Exercise 34

2 Equivalent Ratios

John has 8 cents and Peter has 12 cents.

The ratio of John's money to Peter's money is 8 : 12.

The ratio of John's money to Peter's money is 4 : 6.

The ratio of John's money to Peter's money is 2 : 3.

8 : 12, 4 : 6 and 2 : 3 are **equivalent ratios**.

2 : 3 is a ratio in its simplest form.

1. Write each ratio in its simplest form.

(a) 4 : 10

4 : 10 = ■ : ■

2 is a common factor of 4 and 10.
Divide 4 and 10 by 2.

$\cancel{4} : \cancel{10}$
2 5

(b) 12 : 18

12 : 18 = ■ : ■

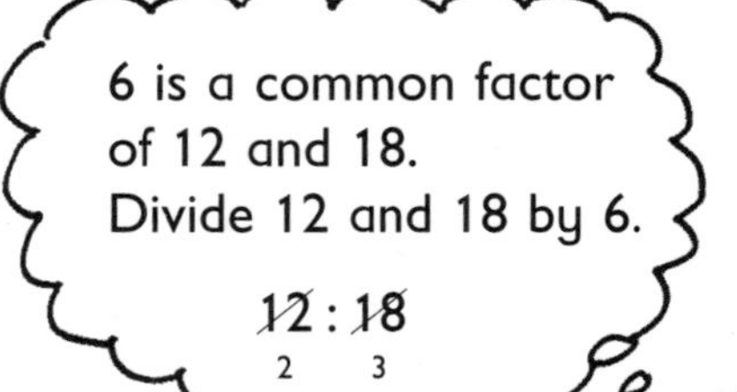

2. Write each ratio in its simplest form.

(a) 8 : 10
(b) 10 : 6
(c) 6 : 24
(d) 21 : 14

3. There are 15 ducks and 12 chickens in a farm. Find the ratio of the number of ducks to the number of chickens.

15 : 12 = ■ : ■

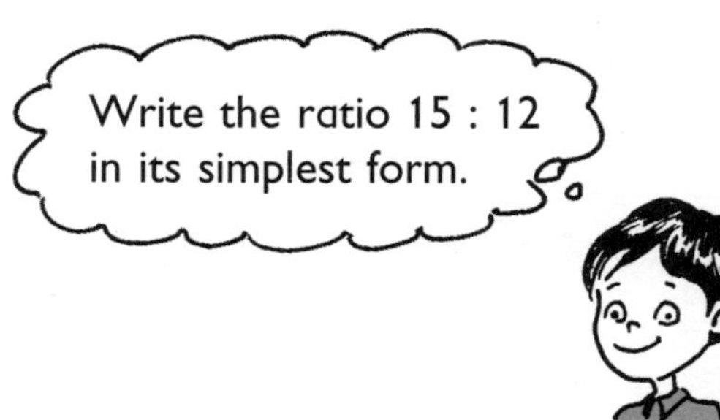

The ratio of the number of ducks to the number of chickens is ■ : ■.

Workbook Exercise 35

4. There are 40 students in a class. 25 of them are boys.
Find the ratio of the number of boys to the number of girls in the class.

Number of girls = 40 – 25 = 15

Number of boys = 25

25 : 15 = ■ : ■

The ratio of the number of boys to the number of girls is ■ : ■.

5. The ratio of the length of Ribbon A to the length of Ribbon B is 7 : 4.
If Ribbon A is 21 m long, find the length of Ribbon B.

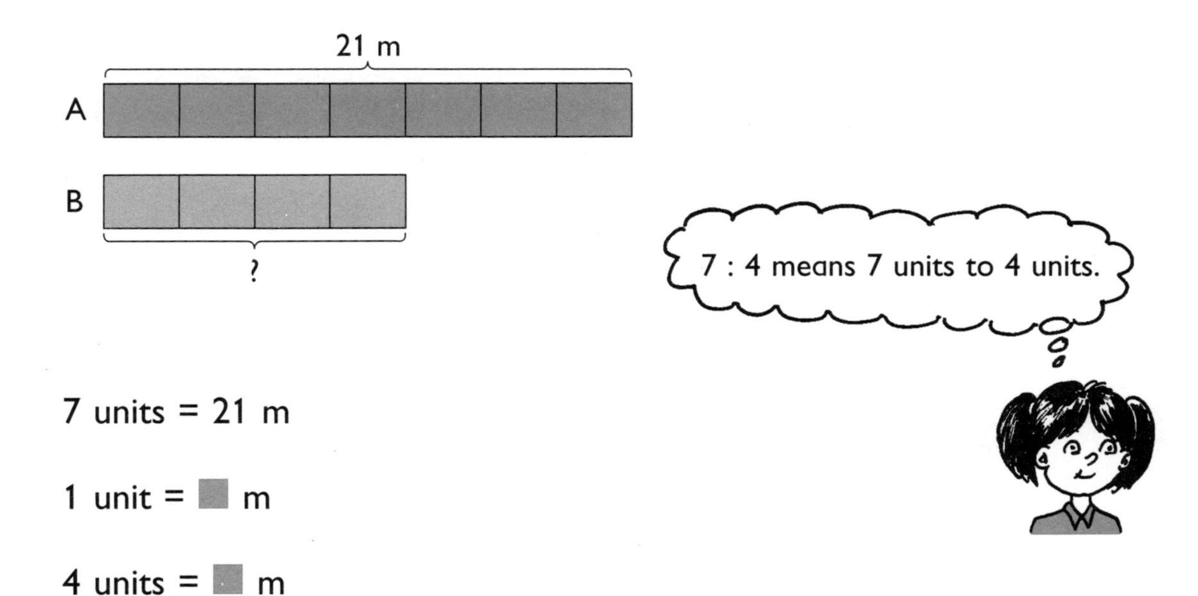

7 units = 21 m

1 unit = ■ m

4 units = ■ m

The length of Ribbon B is ■ m.

6. Siti and Mary shared \$35 in the ratio 4 : 3.
How much money did Siti receive?

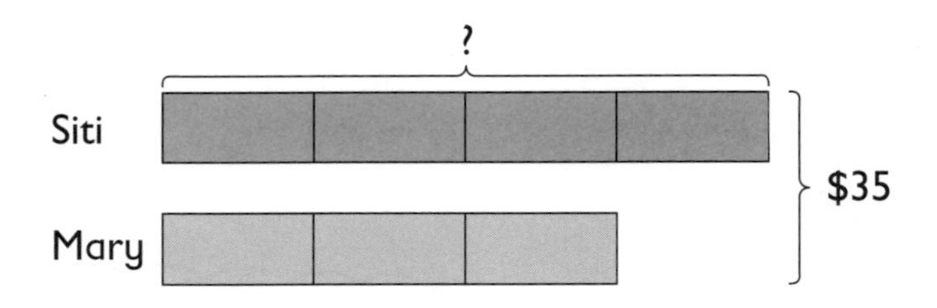

7 units = \$35

1 unit = \$▢

4 units = \$▢

Siti received \$▢.

7. The ratio of the weight of Package X to the weight of Package Y is 5 : 3. If the weight of Package X is 40 kg, find the total weight of the two packages.

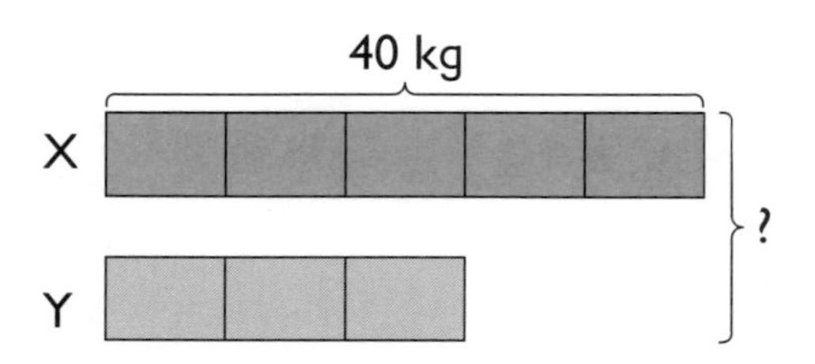

5 units = 40 kg

1 unit = ▢ kg

8 units = ▢ kg

The total weight is ▢ kg.

Workbook Exercise 36

PRACTICE 5A

1.

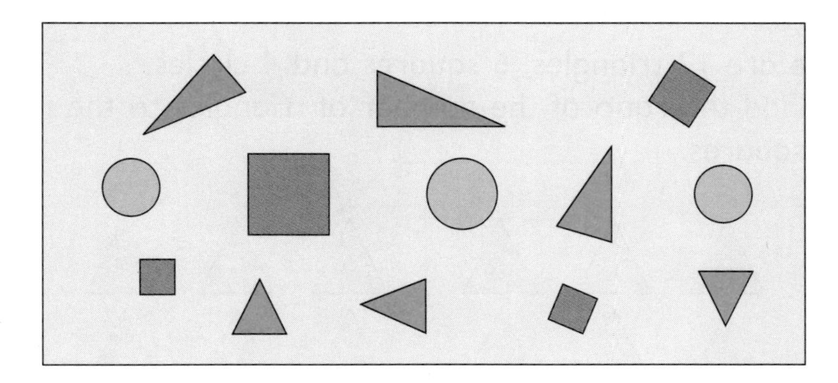

(a) Find the ratio of the number of circles to the number of triangles.

(b) Find the ratio of the number of triangles to the number of squares.

2. The length of a rectangle is 16 cm and its width is 12 cm. Find the ratio of the length of the rectangle to its width.

3. Ali won a cash prize of $50. He saved $35 and spent the rest. Find the ratio of the amount of money he saved to the amount of money he spent.

4. Brianne made pineapple drinks by mixing pineapple syrup and water in the ratio 2 : 7. If she used 4 liters of pineapple syrup, how much water did she use?

5. David cuts a rope 60 m long into two pieces in the ratio 2 : 3. What is the length of the shorter piece of rope?

6. The ratio of Adam's weight to John's weight is 6 : 5. If Adam weighs 48 kg, find John's weight.

7. The ratio of the number of boys to the number of girls is 2 : 5. If there are 100 boys, how many children are there altogether?

3 Comparing Three Quantities

There are 12 triangles, 6 squares and 4 circles.

(a) Find the ratio of the number of triangles to the number of squares.

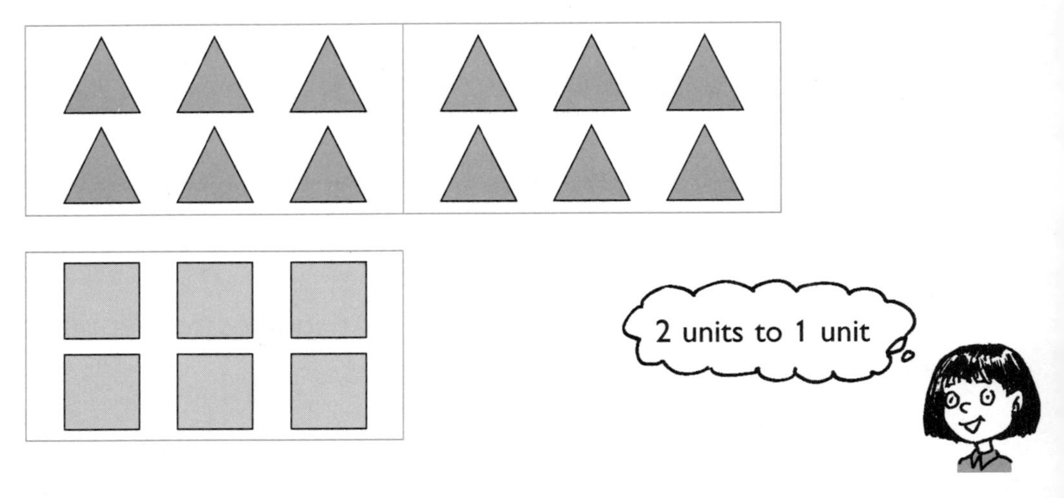

The ratio of the number of triangles to the number of squares is ▇ : ▇.

(b) Find the ratio of the number of triangles to the number of squares to the number of circles.

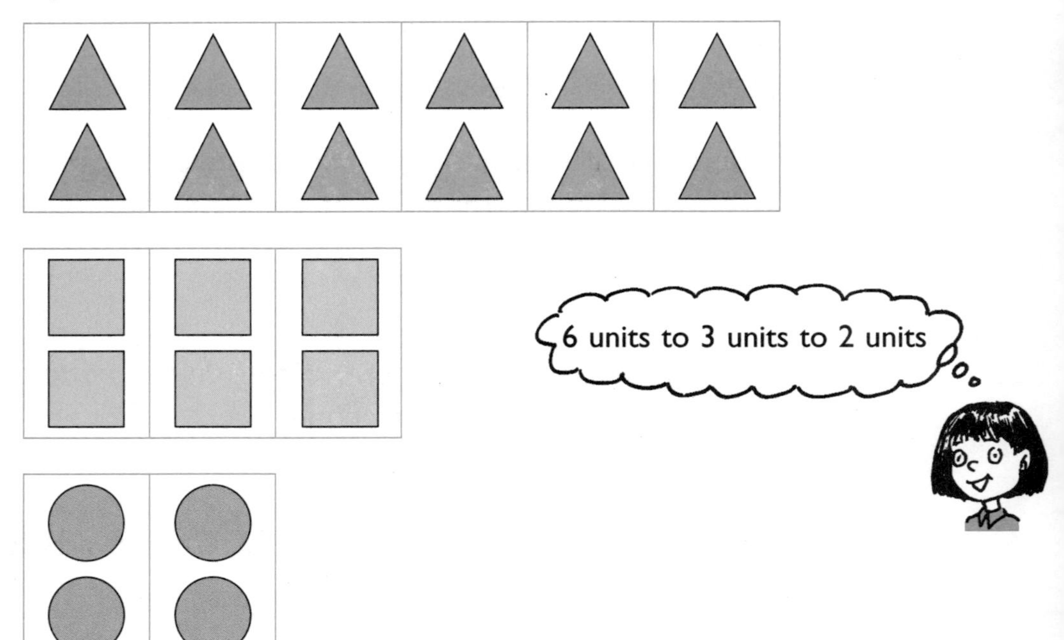

The ratio of the number of triangles to the number of squares to the number of circles is ▇ : ▇ : ▇.

1. Write each ratio in its simplest form.

(a) 12 : 6 : 4

12 : 6 : 4 = ■ : ■ : ■

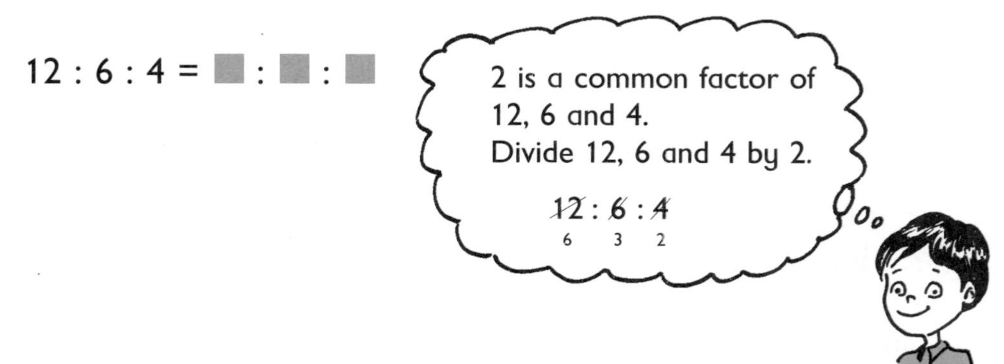

(b) 20 : 10 : 15

20 : 10 : 15 = ■ : ■ : ■

5 is a common factor of
20, 10 and 15.
Divide 20, 10 and 15 by 5.
20 : 10 : 15
4 2 3

2. 20 liters of water are poured into 3 buckets A, B and C in the ratio 2 : 3 : 5.
Find the volume of water in Bucket C.

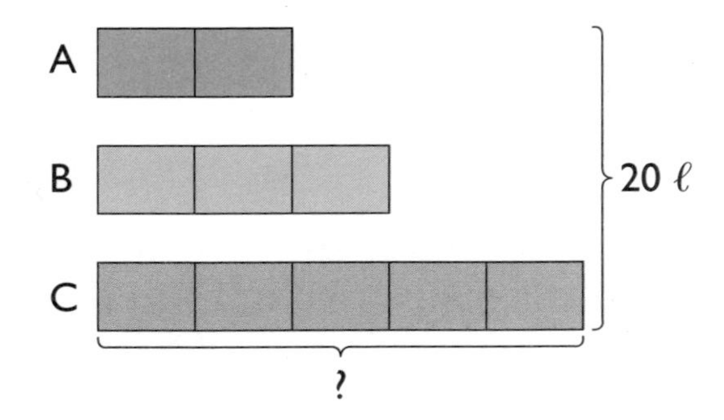

10 units = 20 liters

1 unit = ■ liters

5 units = ■ liters

The volume of water in Bucket C is ■ liters.

Workbook Exercises 37 & 38

PRACTICE 5B

1. In a school, there are 24 female teachers and 10 male teachers. What is the ratio of the number of male teachers to the number of female teachers?

2. In a fruit orchard, there are 60 peach trees, 20 plum trees and 35 apricot trees.
   What is the ratio of the number of peach trees to the number of plum trees to the number of apricot trees?

3. Mrs. Bates cooked oatmeal by adding water to oatmeal in the ratio 3 : 1.
   If she used 12 cups of water, how many cups of oatmeal did she use?

4. In a swimming club, the ratio of the number of boys to the number of girls is 7 : 4.
   If there are 121 children in the swimming club, how many boys are there?

5. William has $120. Steve has $20 less than William. What is the ratio of Steve's money to William's money?

6. A pole, 90 cm long, is painted green, white and black in the ratio 3 : 4 : 2.
   (a) What length of the pole is painted green?
   (b) What length of the pole is painted black?

7. Cement, sand and stone chippings are mixed in the ratio 1 : 2 : 4. The total volume of sand and stone chippings used is 24 m^3.
   (a) Find the volume of cement in the mixture.
   (b) Find the volume of sand in the mixture.

8. The ratio of David's weight to Ryan's weight to Ali's weight is 8 : 5 : 4. If Ryan weighs 30 kg, find the total weight of the 3 boys.

9. 3 boys share a sum of money in the ratio 5 : 3 : 2. If the smallest share is $30, find the biggest share.

6 Angles

1 Measuring Angles

What is the size of $\angle m$?

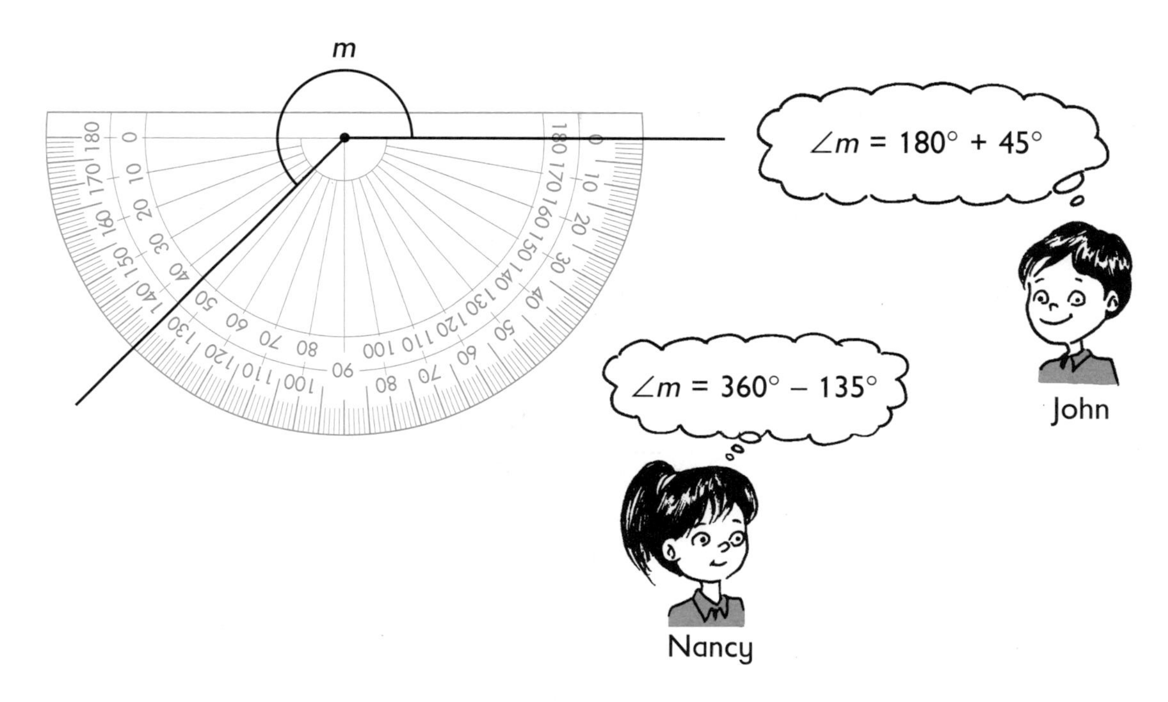

Measure $\angle n$.

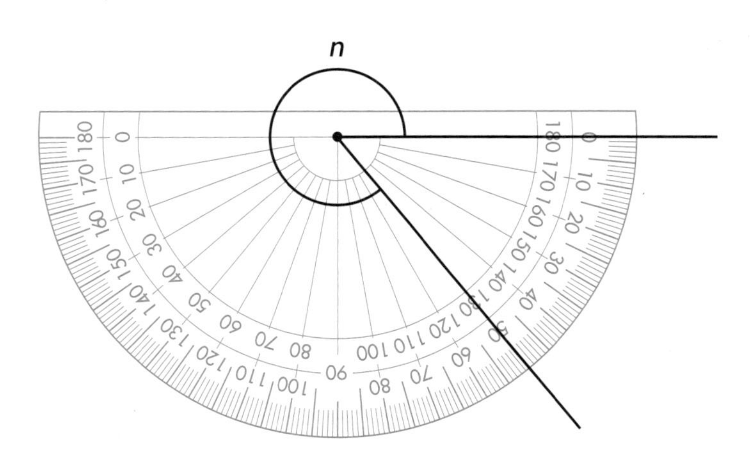

1. Estimate and then find each of the following marked angles by measurement.

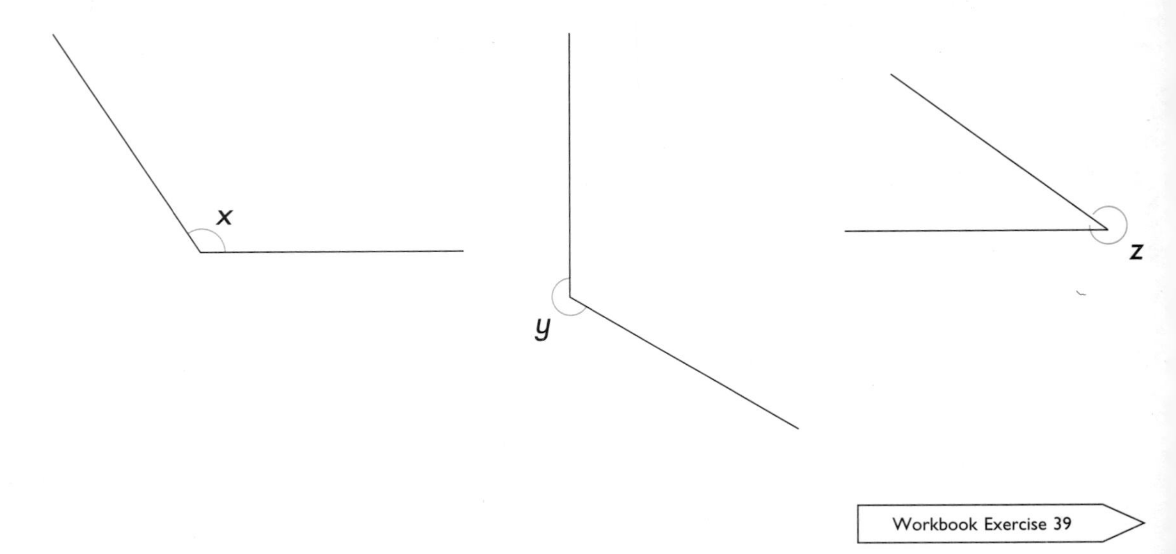

Workbook Exercise 39

2.

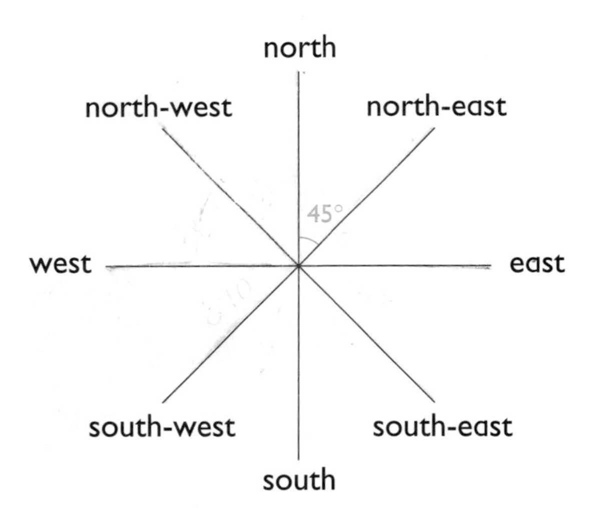

(a) You start facing north and turn clockwise to south-east. What angle do you turn through?

(b) You start facing west and turn counterclockwise to south-west. What angle do you turn through?

3. (a) You start facing north-west and turn clockwise through 90°. Which direction are you facing?

(b) After turning counterclockwise through 225°, you end up facing east.
Which direction were you facing at the start?

Workbook Exercise 40

2 Finding Unknown Angles

When two straight lines cross, they form two pairs of **vertically opposite angles**.

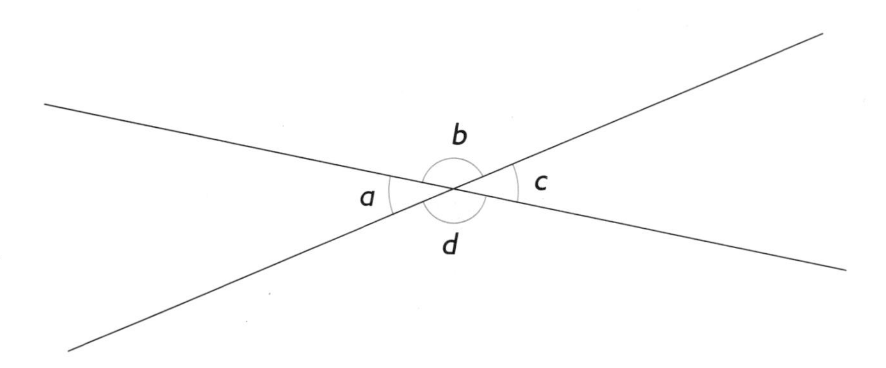

Measure the unknown angles.

$\angle a = 34^\circ$

$\angle b = \square^\circ$

$\angle c = \square^\circ$

$\angle d = \square^\circ$

$\angle a$ and $\angle c$ are vertically opposite angles.
$\angle b$ and $\angle d$ are also vertically opposite angles.

Vertically opposite angles are equal.

$\angle p$, $\angle q$ and $\angle r$ are angles on a straight line. Measure the unknown angles.

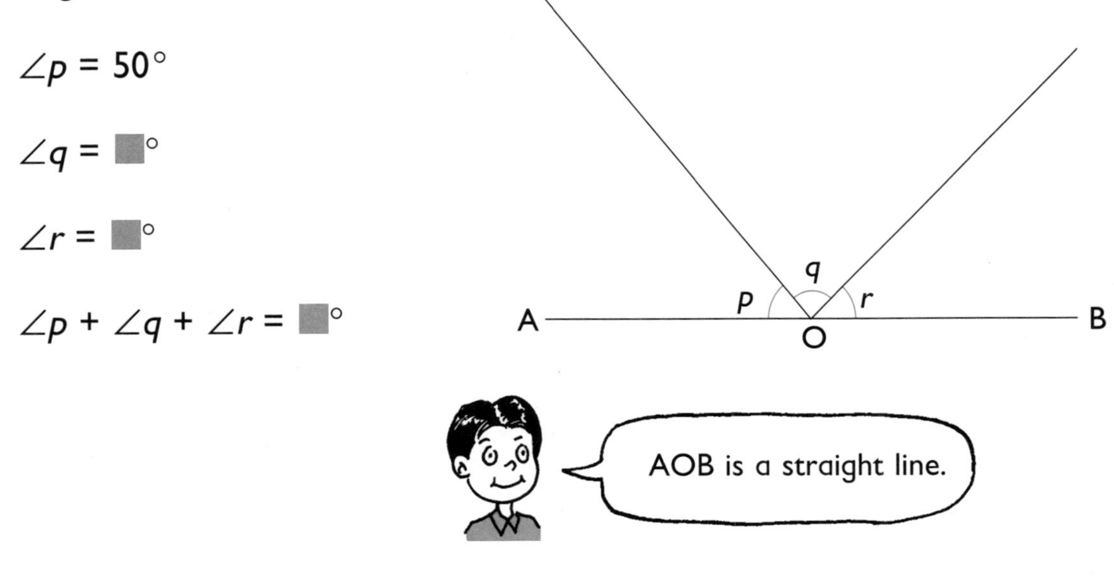

$\angle p = 50^\circ$

$\angle q = \square^\circ$

$\angle r = \square^\circ$

$\angle p + \angle q + \angle r = \square^\circ$

The sum of the angles on a straight line is 180°.

$\angle x$, $\angle y$ and $\angle z$ are angles at a point. Measure the unknown angles.

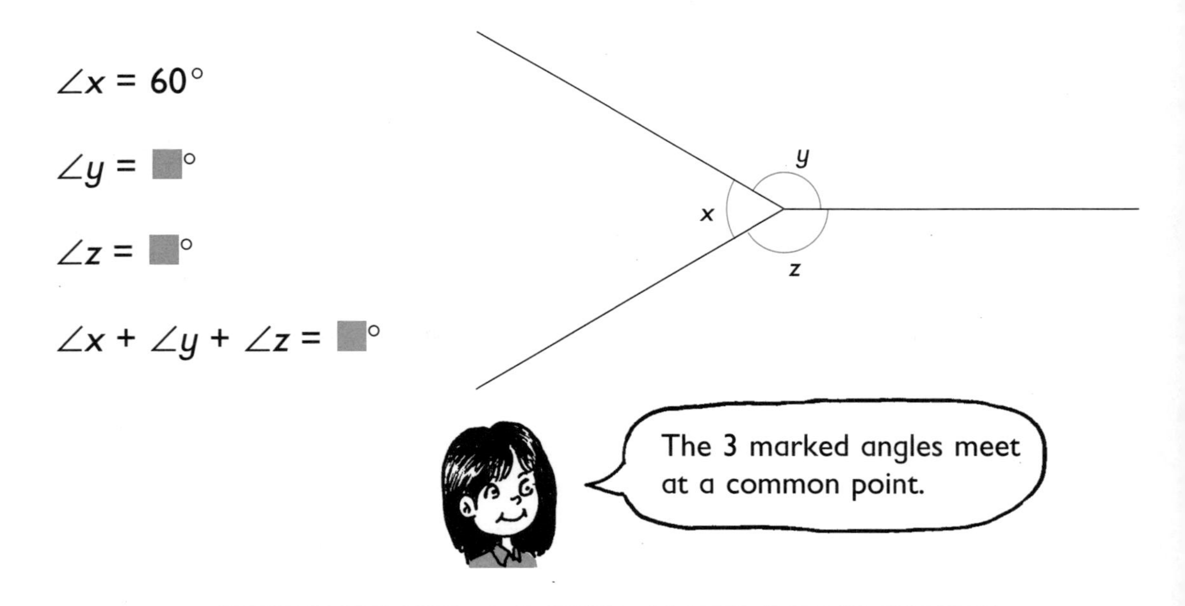

$\angle x = 60^\circ$

$\angle y = \square^\circ$

$\angle z = \square^\circ$

$\angle x + \angle y + \angle z = \square^\circ$

The sum of the angles at a point is 360°.

1. Find the unknown marked angle in each of the following:

(a)

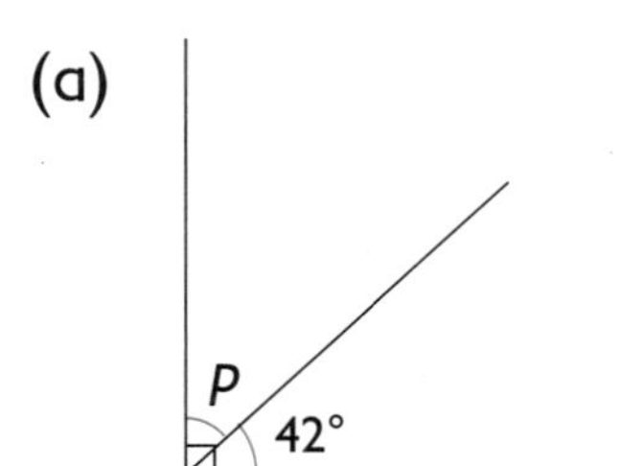

$\angle p = 90^\circ - 42^\circ = $ ■$^\circ$

(b)

q

37°

$\angle q = 180^\circ - 37^\circ = $ ■$^\circ$

(c)

r

15°

$\angle r = 360^\circ - 15^\circ = $ ■$^\circ$

2. The figure shows 4 angles formed by two straight lines.
If $\angle w = 46^\circ$, find $\angle x$, $\angle y$ and $\angle z$.

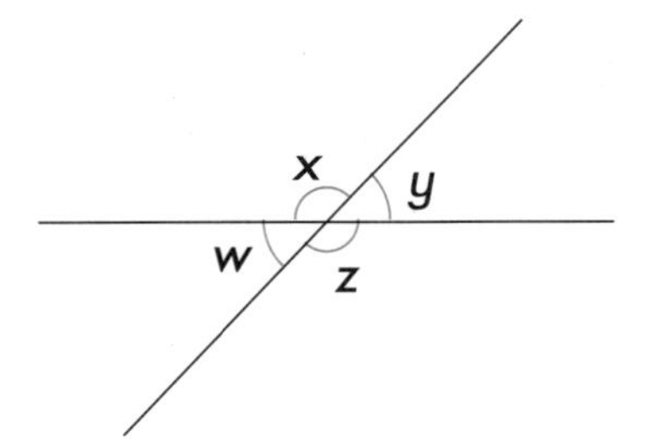

3. In the figure, AOB and COD are straight lines. Find $\angle$COB.

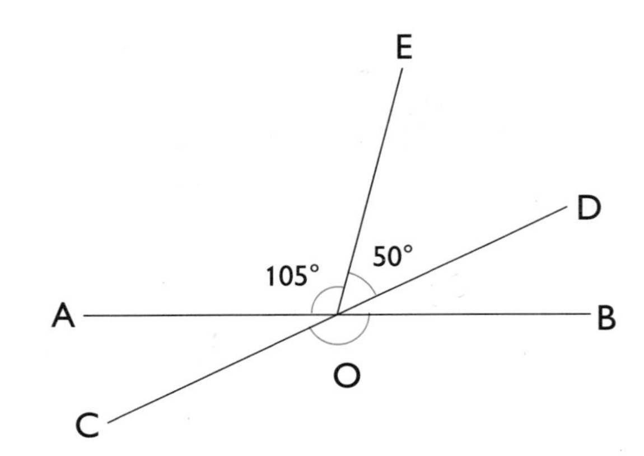

4. In the figure, ABC is a straight line.
$\angle ABD = 35°$ and $\angle EBC = 55°$. Find $\angle DBE$.

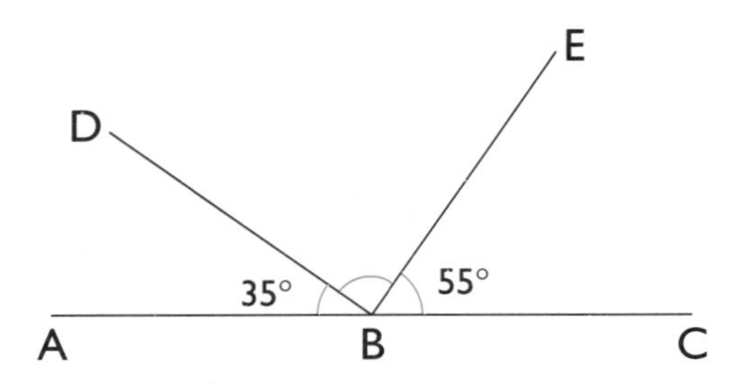

$\angle DBE = 180° - 35° - 55°$

5. In the figure, find $\angle x$.

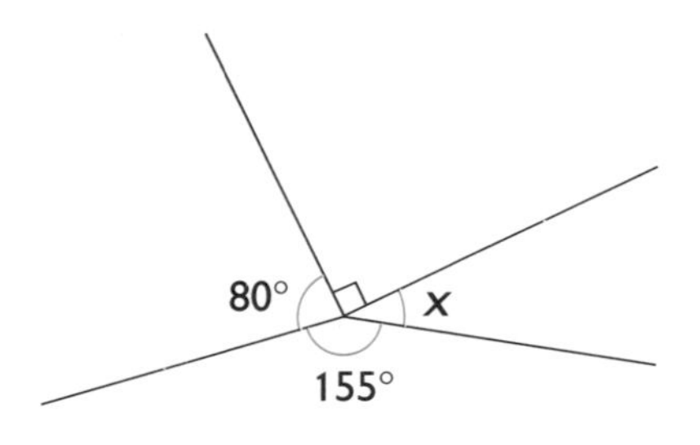

6. In the figure, find $\angle m$ and $\angle n$.

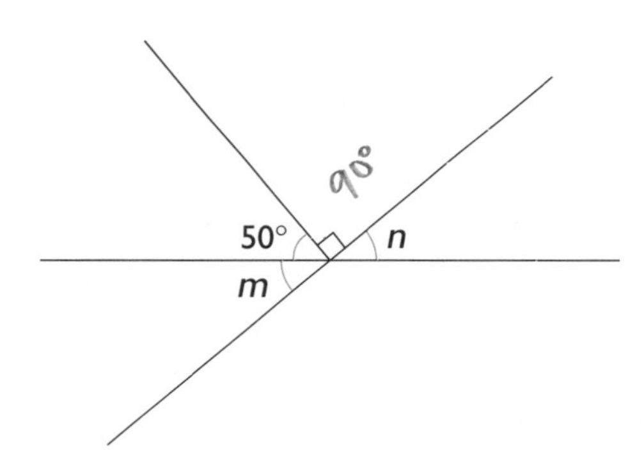

$\angle m$ and $\angle n$ are vertically opposite angles.

7. Find the unknown marked angles.

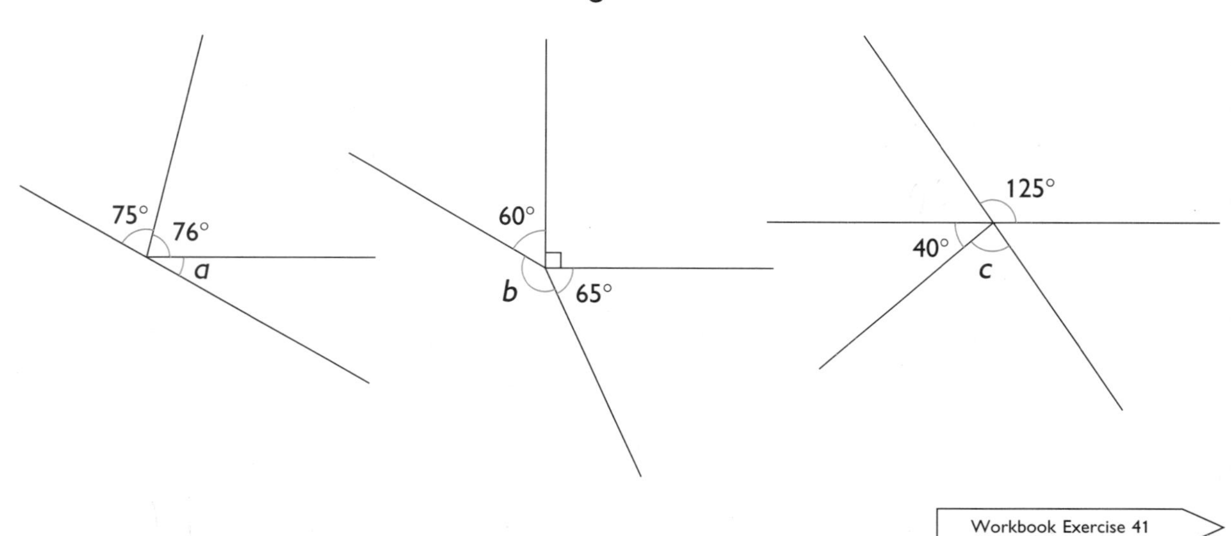

Workbook Exercise 41

REVIEW B

1. What number is 1000 less than 20,000?

2. Juan bought a car for $42,680.
   Round off this amount of money to the nearest $1000.

3. Find the value of each of the following:
   (a) 670×10 (b) 728×100 (c) 350×1000
   (d) $4300 \div 10$ (e) $58,000 \div 100$ (f) $628,000 \div 1000$

4. If ☆☆☆☆☆ represent 60, what number do ☆☆ represent?

5. What fraction of 3 ℓ is 800 ml?

6. Steven had 24 pineapples. He sold 6 of them. What fraction of the pineapples did he sell?

7. An examination lasted $2\frac{1}{4}$ hours.
   Express $2\frac{1}{4}$ hours in hours and minutes.

8. A necklace is $\frac{3}{5}$ m long. Express $\frac{3}{5}$ m in centimeters.

9. Lily has $25. Mary has $10 more than Lily. Amber has 3 times as much money as Mary.
   (a) How much money does Amber have?
   (b) How much more money than Lily does Amber have?
   (c) How much money do the 3 girls have altogether?

10. Lynn bought 8 m of string. She used $\frac{5}{8}$ of the string to make a flower-pot hanger. How much of the string did she have left?

11. Natalie cuts a raffia $\frac{4}{5}$ m long into 8 pieces of equal length. What is the length of each piece of raffia? Give the answer in meters.

12. Matthew had 64 watermelons. He sold $\frac{3}{4}$ of them. How many watermelons did he sell?

13. Mrs. Gray had 2 kg of flour. She used $\frac{2}{5}$ of it to make buns. How much flour did she have left? Give the answer in kilograms.

14. There are 1500 workers in a factory. $\frac{5}{6}$ of them are men. $\frac{3}{10}$ of the men are single. How many single male workers are there in the factory?

15. Lauren spent $\frac{3}{5}$ of her money on a refrigerator. The refrigerator cost $756. How much money did she have left?

16. Dan saved twice as much as Brett. Maria saved $60 more than Brett. If they saved $600 altogether, how much did Maria save?

17. Brett picked 257 cherries from one tree and 493 from another. He sold all the cherries at 50 for $3. How much money did he receive?

18. Charles bought 40 boxes of oranges for $258. There were 24 oranges in each box. He threw away 15 rotten oranges and sold the rest at 3 for $1. How much money did he make?

19. John and Peter share $180 in the ratio 3 : 2. How much more money does John receive than Peter?

20. The ratio of the length of a rectangular field to its width is 4 : 3. The length of the field is 20 m. Find its area and perimeter.

21. Sean, Ryan and John shared a sum of money in the ratio 3 : 4 : 5. If Sean received $30, what was the sum of money shared?

22. Find the area and the perimeter of the shaded figure.

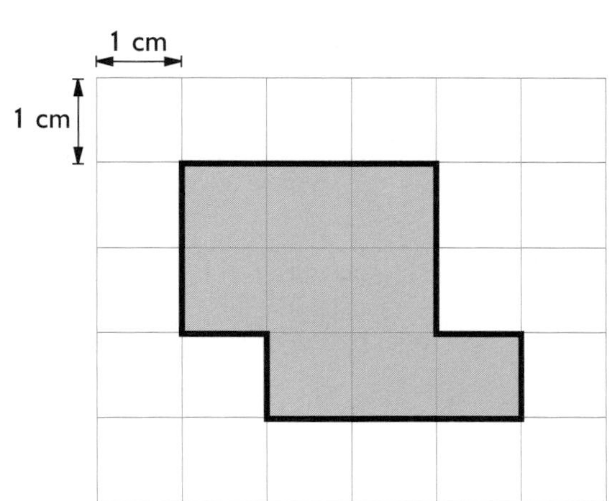

23. Find the perimeter and area of each figure. (All the angles are right angles.)

(a)

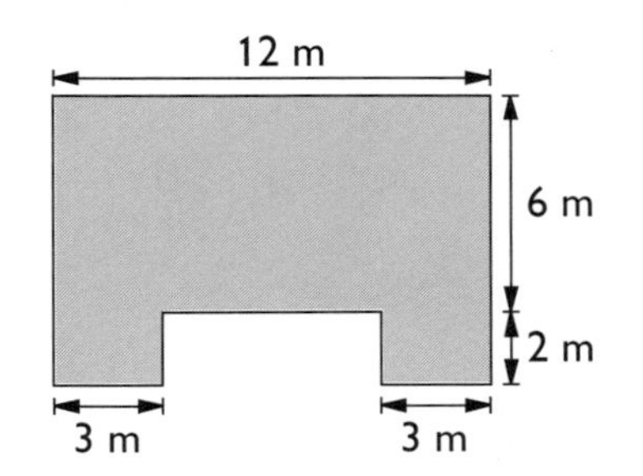

(b)

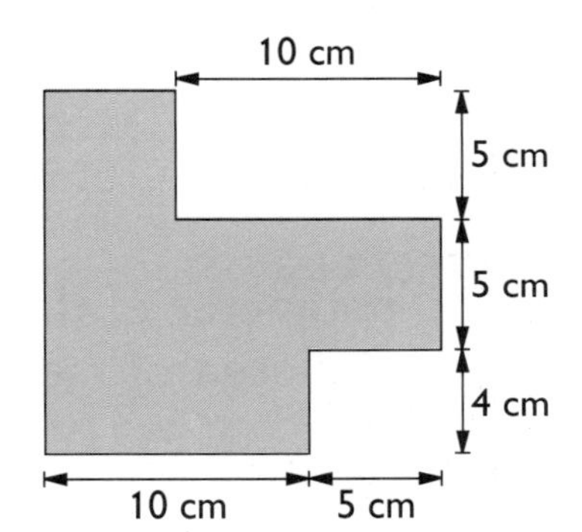

24. Estimate and then find the marked angles by measurement.

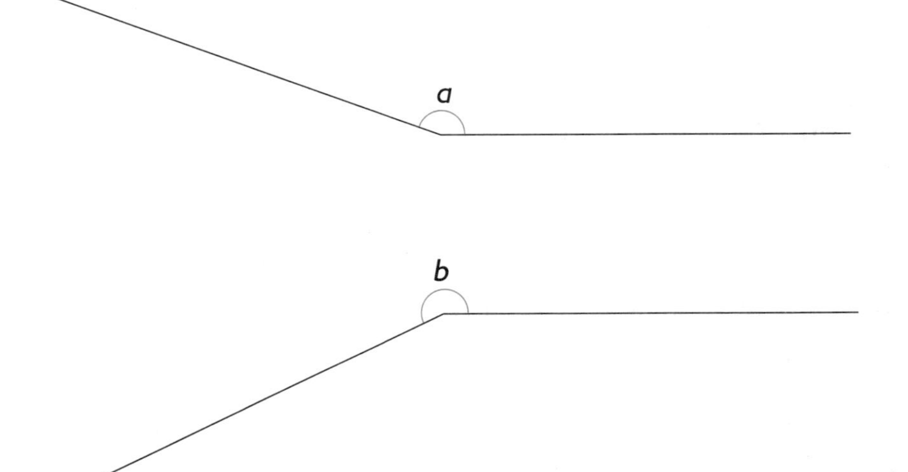

25. In each of the following figures, not drawn to scale, find $\angle x$.

(a)

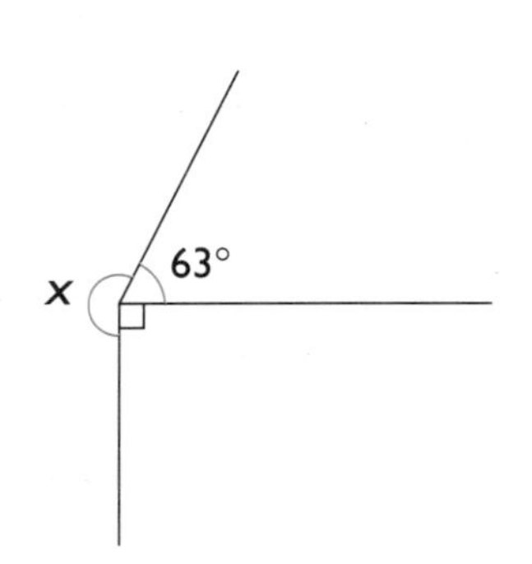

(b)

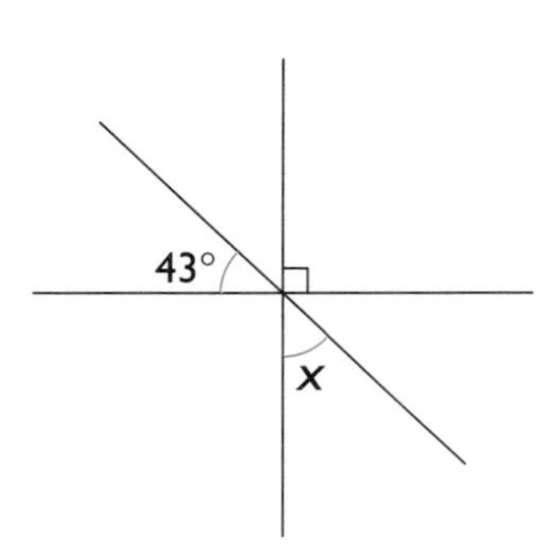

26. Find the area of each shaded triangle.

(a)

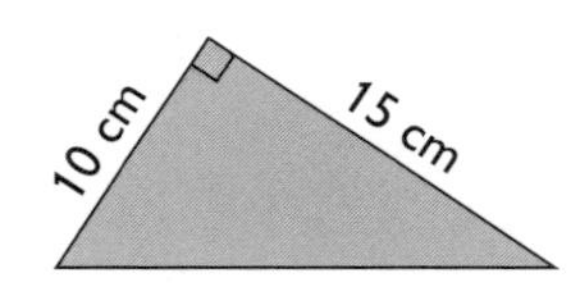

(b)

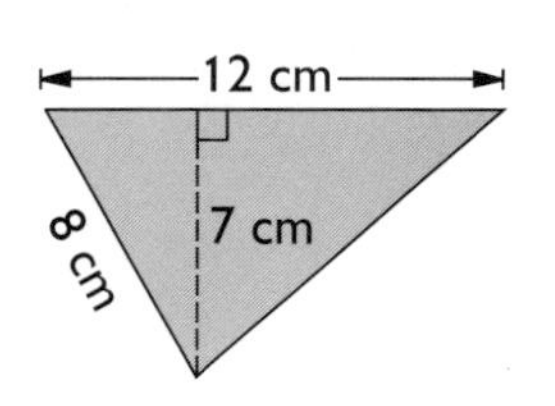

(c)

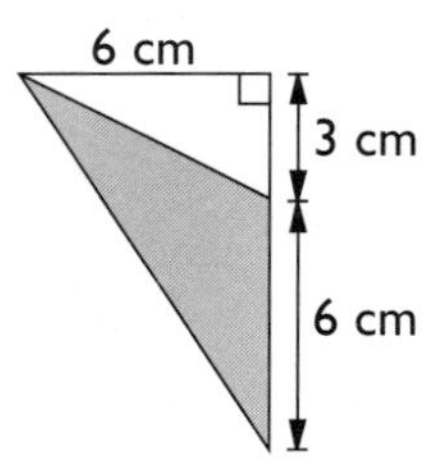

27. The perimeter of the triangle is 36 m.
Find the area of the triangle.

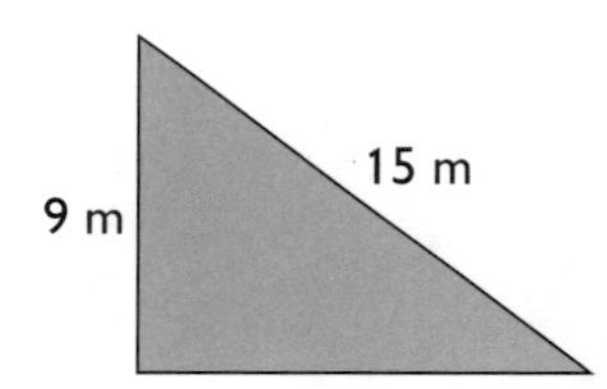

28. Find the shaded area of each rectangle.

(a)

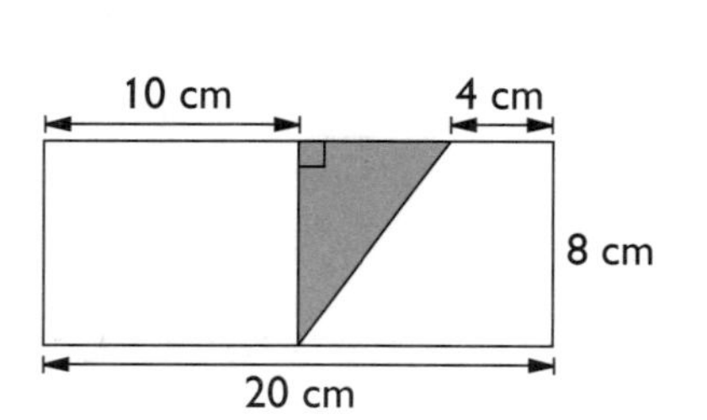

(b)

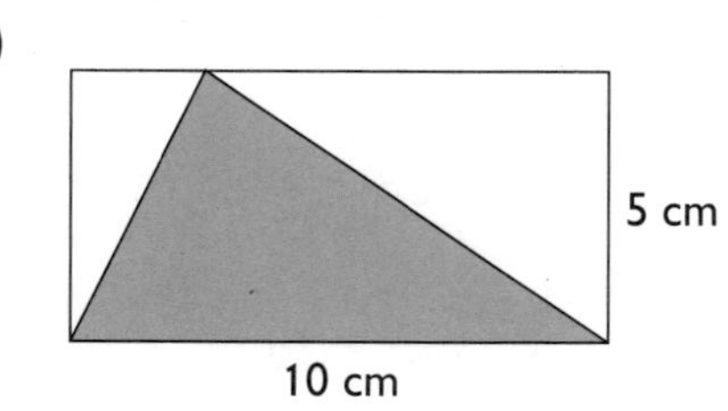

(c)

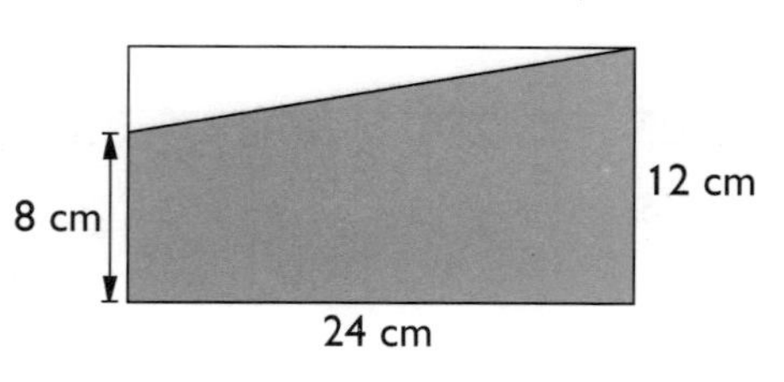

(d)

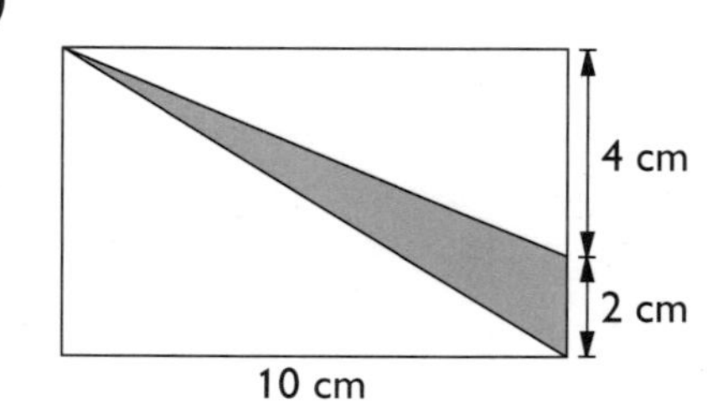

REVIEW C

1. A plane traveled 5840 mi.
   Round off this distance to the nearest 100 mi.

2. David is 17 lb lighter than Pablo. Their total weight is 259 lb.
   Find David's weight.

3. Water is poured equally into 4 containers. Each container has 5 c of water. How many quarts of water are there in the four containers?

4. Mrs. Anderson bought 5 yd of cloth. She used the cloth to make 12 napkins of the same size. How much cloth did she use for each napkin?
   (Give the answer in feet.)

5. Adam poured 4 qt of milk equally into 5 jugs.
   How much milk was there in each jug?
   (Give the answer in quarts.)

6. A crate of strawberries weighing 8 lb was divided into 12 equal shares. What was the weight of each share?
   (Give the answer in ounces as a mixed fraction.)

7. How many cubic inches are there in a cubic foot?

8. (a) What fraction of 3 lb is 8 oz?
   (b) What fraction of 2 gal is 3 qt?
   (c) What fraction of 2 qt is 4 c?

9. A ribbon is $\frac{3}{4}$ ft long. Express $\frac{3}{4}$ ft in inches.

10. Mrs. Garcia had 6 lb of flour. She used $\frac{1}{5}$ of it to make bread.

    How much flour was left?
    (Give the answer in pounds.)

11. The ratio of the length of a rectangular field to its width is 5 : 2. The length of the field is 30 yd. Find its perimeter and area.

12. Find the perimeter and area of each figure.
(All the angles are right angles.)

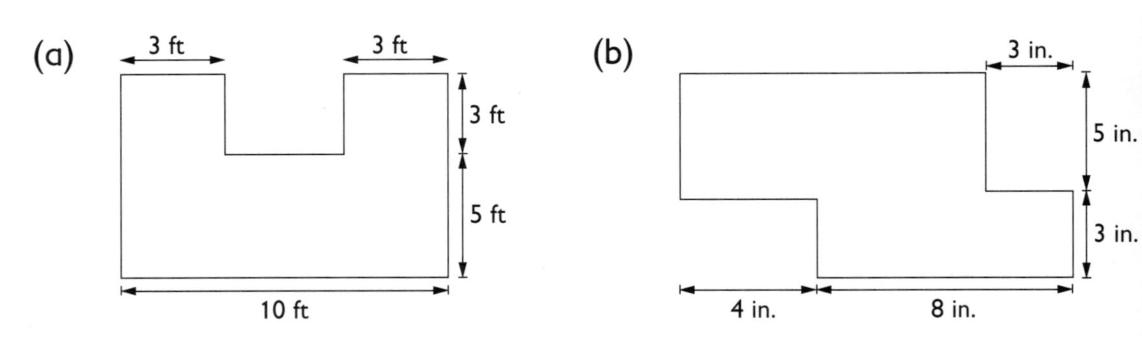

13. A cook used $2\frac{1}{4}$ gal of oil last week. Express $2\frac{1}{4}$ gal in gallons and cups.

14. Mrs. Goldberg used 8.7 ft of lace for 5 pillow cases. If she used an equal length of lace for each pillow case, how much lace did she use for each pillow case?
(Give the answer in feet.)

15. The area of a square is 81 in.^{2}
Find its perimeter.

16. Emily bought a bag of candies which weighed 1 lb 11 oz.
She gave away 15 oz of candy.
How many ounces of candy was left?

17. Write in feet and inches.
(a) 18 in. (b) 28 in. (c) 57 in.

18. Find the volume of a cube of length 6 in.

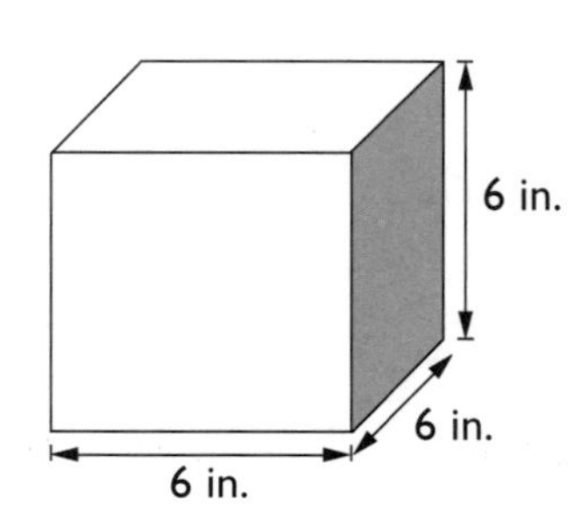

19. A cuboid measures 12 ft long, 6 ft wide and 7 ft high. Find its volume.

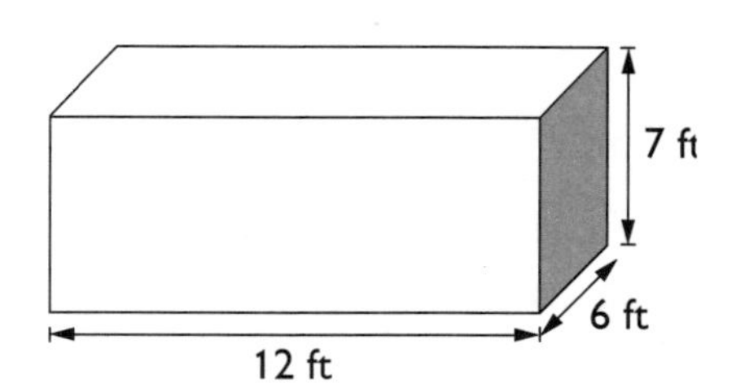

20. $\frac{2}{3}$ of a jug of water is 6 c.
Find the total number of cups of water in the jug.

21. Ryan drinks 2 c of milk a day.
How much milk does he drink in three weeks?
(Give the answer in quarts and cups.)

22. Multiply in compound units. Give the answer in compound units.
(a) 3 yd 2 ft × 7 = ____ yd ____ ft
(b) 5 lb 14 oz × 3 = ____ lb ____ oz
(c) 4 gal 3 qt × 5 = ____ gal ____ qt
(d) 2 ft 11 in. × 2 = ____ ft ____ in.

23. Divide in compound units.
(a) 3 yd 1 ft ÷ 2 = ____ yd ____ ft
(b) 2 lb 10 oz ÷ 6 = ____ lb ____ oz
(c) 6 gal 3 qt ÷ 3 = ____ gal ____ qt
(d) 2 ft 8 in. ÷ 4 = ____ ft ____ in.

24. A rope was cut into three equal pieces. Each piece was 1 ft 6 in. long.
What was the length of the rope?
(Give the answer in feet and inches.)

25. Find the value of the following:

(a) $\frac{1}{3}$ of 24 yd

(b) $\frac{4}{5}$ of 35 in.

(c) $1\frac{1}{2}$ of 14 oz

(d) $\frac{5}{6}$ of 12 gal

26. A basket weighs 12 oz. A watermelon weighing 7 lb 9 oz is added to the basket. What is the total weight of the basket and watermelon? (Give the answer in pounds and ounces.)

27. Mitchell jogged 2.2 mi on Friday.
He jogged 0.7 mi less on Saturday than on Friday.
What was the total distance he jogged on the two days?

28. The total weight of 5 bars of chocolate and a bag of sugar is 3.4 lb. If the weight of the bag of sugar is 1.1 lb, find the weight of each bar of chocolate.

29.

Beef	\$3.50 per lb
Chicken	\$1.95 per lb

Mrs. Campbell bought $\frac{1}{2}$ lb of beef and 2 lb of chicken. How much did she spend?

30. Round off 258.76 lb to 1 decimal place.

31. Which is greatest?
2.5 ft, 37 in., 25 in., 2.25 ft, 0.5 yd

32. The total weight of Morgan, Emily and Ashley is 243 lb. Morgan is 30 lb heavier than Emily. Emily is 6 lb lighter than Ashley. What is Ashley's weight?